W9-BUF-665

WILLIAM K. DURR • JEAN M. LE PERE • RUTH BROWN

CONSULTANT • **PAUL McKEE**

LINGUISTIC ADVISOR • **JACK E. KITTELL**

FIESTA

HOUGHTON MIFFLIN COMPANY • BOSTON

ATLANTA · DALLAS · GENEVA, ILLINOIS · HOPEWELL, NEW JERSEY · PALO ALTO

Acknowledgments

For each of the selections listed below, grateful acknowledgment is made for permission to adapt and/or reprint copyrighted material, as follows:

"At the Baseball Game Sat Mrs. Pace," by Harriet Mandelbaum. Reprinted from *The Limerick Book,* compiled by Miriam Troop. Copyright © 1964 by Grosset & Dunlap, Inc., by permission of the publisher.

"Autumn Thought." From *The Dream Keeper,* by Langston Hughes. Copyright 1932 by Alfred A. Knopf, Inc. and renewed 1960 by Langston Hughes. Reprinted by permission of the publisher.

"Beauty." From *I Am a Pueblo Indian Girl,* by E-Yeh-Shure'. Reprinted by permission of William Morrow and Company, Inc. Copyright © 1939 by William Morrow and Company, Inc.

"Before You Spend That Coin . . ." From *The Adventure Book of Money* by Eva Knox Evans. © 1956 by Capitol Publishing Company; reprinted by permission of Western Publishing Company, Inc.

"Beware, My Child," by Shel Silverstein, reprinted with the permission of the author.

"Brave Kate Shelley," from *Clear the Track* by Louis Wolfe. Copyright, 1952, by Louis Wolfe. Published by J. B. Lippincott Company.

"The Camel," by Ogden Nash, copyright 1933 by The Curtis Publishing Company. Reprinted by permission of Little, Brown and Company and J. M. Dent & Sons, Ltd.

"Camel in the Sea," from *A Camel in the Sea* by Lee Garrett Goetz. Copyright © 1966 by Lee Garrett Goetz and Paul Galdone. Used by permission of the publisher, McGraw-Hill Book Company.

"The Case of the Mysterious Tramp," by Donald J. Sobol. Copyright 1966 Donald J. Sobol, *Encyclopedia Brown Finds the Clues,* published by Thomas Nelson & Sons.

"Commands," by Harriet Carlson. From *The Instructor.* © The Instructor Publications, Inc. November 1967.

"A Crust of Bread," reprinted from *A Crust of Bread* by Andre Drucker. Adapted by permission of the author and the University of London Press, Ltd., publishers.

"Desert Traders," by Iona S. Hiser. Used by permission of the author. Reprinted by special permission from *Jack and Jill* Magazine (1958). The Curtis Publishing Company.

"Doctoring an Elephant," from *Zoo Doctor* by William Bridges. Reprinted by permission of William Morrow and Company, Inc. Copyright 1957, William Bridges.

"The Duck," from *Verses from 1929 On* by Ogden Nash. Reprinted by permission of Little, Brown and Company. Copyright 1936 by The Curtis Publishing Company. British rights granted by J. M. Dent and Sons, Ltd.

"E Is the Escalator," from *All Around the Town* by Phyllis McGinley. Copyright, 1948, by Phyllis McGinley. Published by J. B. Lippincott Company. British rights granted by Curtis Brown, Ltd.

"Fats, the Big Operator," by Marion Holland. Adapted with the author's permission. Originally appeared in *Story Parade.*

"Goldfish," from *Don't Ever Cross a Crocodile* by Kaye Starbird. Copyright © 1963 by Kaye Starbird. Published by J. B. Lippincott Company.

"The Herons on Bo Island," from *By Bog and Sea in Donegal* by Elizabeth Shane. Reprinted by permission of Hutchinson and Company, Ltd.

"His Majesty, the Peasant," by Sally Werner. Reprinted by special permission from *Jack and Jill* Magazine © 1958 The Curtis Publishing Company.

"A House for Aquanauts." Our thanks to General Electric Company for their helpful pictures and information.

"In the Fog," by Lilian Moore. Copyright © 1967 by Lilian Moore. From *I Feel the Same Way.* Used by permission of Atheneum Publishers.

"The Leaf Pile," from *A Snail's a Failure Socially* by Kaye Starbird. Copyright © 1966 by Kaye Starbird. Published by J. B. Lippincott Company.

"Marco Comes Late," by Dr. Seuss. Reprinted by permission of Ashley Famous Agency, Inc. Copyright © 1950 by Dr. Seuss.

1973 IMPRESSION

PRINTED IN THE U. S. A.

ISBN: 0-395-00584-1

"A Minor Bird." From *You Come Too* by Robert Frost. Copyright 1928 by Holt, Rinehart and Winston, Inc. Copyright © 1956 by Robert Frost. Reprinted by permission of Holt, Rinehart and Winston, Inc. and by Jonathan Cape Ltd.

"Mischievous Meg" Story Treasure: "Meg Experiments to See if She Is Clairvoyant." Adapted from *Mischievous Meg* by Astrid Lindgren. Copyright © 1960 by Astrid Lindgren. Reprinted by permission of The Viking Press, Inc. British rights granted by Oxford University Press.

"Mystery Guest at Left End," by Beman Lord. *Mystery Guest at Left End* by Beman Lord. Copyright © 1964 by Beman Lord. Used by permission of Henry Z. Walck, Inc.

"Paul Bunyan Swings His Axe" Story Treasure, by Dell J. McCormick. Adapted with the author's permission from *Paul Bunyan Swings His Axe,* published by The Caxton Printers, Ltd., 1936.

"The Problem," from *A Snail's a Failure Socially* by Kaye Starbird. Copyright © 1966 by Kaye Starbird. Published by J. B. Lippincott Company.

"A Ride on High," by Candida Palmer. *A Ride on High* by Candida Palmer is Copyright © 1966 by Ruth Candida Palmer. Published by J. B. Lippincott Company.

"Ronnie and the Admiral," by Jack Bechdolt. Used with permission of the author's estate (Mr. and Mrs. H. J. Merwin). Originally published in *Story Parade* Magazine.

"Rupert Piper Becomes a Hero." From *The Terrible Troubles of Rupert Piper* by Ethelyn M. Parkinson. Story copyright © 1955 assigned to Abingdon Press. Used by permission.

"Summer," from *Don't Ever Cross a Crocodile* by Kaye Starbird. Copyright © 1963 by Kaye Starbird. Published by J. B. Lippincott Company.

"There Once Was a Gentle Young Knight," by Harriet Mandelbaum. Reprinted from *The Limerick Book,* compiled by Miriam Troop. Copyright © 1964 by Grosset & Dunlap, Inc., by permission of the publisher.

"There Was a Young Queen Named Alice," by Barbara Clemons. Used by permission of the author.

"A Time to Talk." From *You Come Too* by Robert Frost. Copyright 1916 by Holt, Rinehart and Winston, Inc. Copyright 1944 by Robert Frost. Reprinted by permission of Holt, Rinehart and Winston, Inc. and by Jonathan Cape Ltd.

"To Be Answered in Our Next Issue." From *A Way of Knowing,* compiled by Gerald D. McDonald.

"Two Weeks Old and On His Own." From *Peek the Piper* by Vitali Bianki, translated by S. K. Lederer; reprinted by permission of the publisher. Copyright © 1964 by George Braziller, Inc.

"The Umpire," by Milton Bracker. Copyright © 1962 by The New York Times Company. Reprinted by permission.

"A Visit to the Mayor," by Nellie Burchardt. Adapted from *Project Cat* by Nellie Burchardt, copyright 1966, Franklin Watts, Inc.

"Visitors," by Harry Behn. From *The Wizard in the Well,* © 1956 by Harry Behn. Reprinted by permission of Harcourt, Brace and World, Inc.

"We Must Be Polite," by Carl Sandburg. From *Complete Poems,* copyright, 1950, by Carl Sandburg. Reprinted by permission or Harcourt, Brace and World, Inc.

"What Is Green?" by Mary O'Neill. "What Is Green?" copyright © 1961 by Mary Le Duc O'Neill, from *Hailstones and Halibut Bones* by Mary O'Neill. Reprinted by permission of Doubleday and Company, Inc. British rights granted by The World's Work, Ltd.

"Wind Song," by Lilian Moore. Copyright © 1966 by Scholastic Magazines, Inc. From *I Feel the Same Way* by Lilian Moore. Used by permission of Atheneum Publishers.

"Winnie-the-Pooh" Story Treasure: "In Which Pooh and Piglet Go Hunting and Nearly Catch a Woozle." From the book *Winnie-the-Pooh* by A. A. Milne. Illustrated by E. H. Shepard. Copyright, 1926, by E. P. Dutton & Company, Inc. Renewal, 1954, by A. A. Milne. Reprinted by permission of the publishers. British rights granted by Methuen & Co. Ltd., London.

Our thanks to the National Baseball Hall of Fame and Museum, Inc., for granting permission to reproduce Norman Rockwell's painting, "The Three Umpires," on page 137.

Contents

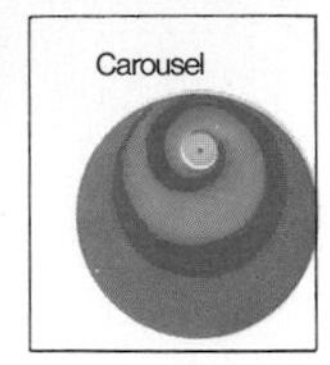

CAROUSEL

STORIES

9 A Visit to the Mayor *by Nellie Burchardt*
28 Doctoring an Elephant *by William Bridges*
42 Ronnie and the Admiral *by Jack Bechdolt*
66 Fats, the Big Operator *by Marion Holland*
96 *A Story Treasure from* Paul Bunyan Swings His Axe *by Dell J. McCormick*

POEMS

27 Autumn Thought *by Langston Hughes*
40 Goldfish *by Kaye Starbird*
60 In the Fog *by Lilian Moore*
81 Beware, My Child *by Shel Silverstein*
95 The Problem *by Kaye Starbird*

INFORMATIONAL ARTICLE

82 Before You Spend That Coin . . . *by Eva Knox Evans*

SKILLS LESSONS

61 *Skill Lesson 1:* Recognizing and Understanding Similes
90 *Skill Lesson 2:* Recognizing and Understanding Metaphors
108 *BIBLIOGRAPHY*

MASQUERADES

STORIES

112 Mystery Guest at Left End *by Beman Lord*
140 A Crust of Bread *by Andre Drucker*
186 A Ride on High *by Candida Palmer*

206 Two Weeks Old and On His Own *by Vitali Bianki*
226 *A Story Treasure from* Winnie-the-Pooh *by A. A. Milne*

POEMS

111 A Minor Bird *by Robert Frost*
137 The Umpire *by Milton Bracker*
137 At the Baseball Game Sat Mrs. Pace *by Harriet Mandelbaum*
158 Beauty *by E-Yeh-Shure'*
172 Summer *by Kaye Starbird*
172 As to the Restless Brook *by John Kendrick Bangs*
173 Limericks *by Harriet Mandelbaum and Barbara Clemons*
185 There Was a Naughty Boy *by John Keats*
198 E Is the Escalator *by Phyllis McGinley*
200 Marco Comes Late *by Dr. Seuss*
223 The Leaf Pile *by Kaye Starbird*
224 The Herons on Bo Island *by Elizabeth Shane*

INFORMATIONAL ARTICLES

138 A House for Aquanauts
160 Jazz

SKILLS LESSONS

167 *Skill Lesson 3:* Recognizing Paragraph Topics
216 *Skill Lesson 4:* Getting Help from Commas

PLAY

174 His Majesty, the Peasant *by Sally Werner*

FUN AND GAMES

199 Two Magic Numbers
236 *BIBLIOGRAPHY*

FANTASIA

STORIES

240 Camel in the Sea *by Lee Garrett Goetz*
265 Brave Kate Shelley *by Louis Wolfe*
284 The Case of the Mysterious Tramp *by Donald J. Sobol*
296 Rupert Piper Becomes a Hero *by Ethelyn Parkinson*
322 *A Story Treasure from* Mischievous Meg *by Astrid Lindgren*

POEMS

239 A Time to Talk *by Robert Frost*
263 The Camel *and* The Duck *by Ogden Nash*
264 Visitors *by Harry Behn*
281 Wind Song *by Lilian Moore*
295 To Be Answered in Our Next Issue *Author Unknown*
314 We Must Be Polite *by Carl Sandburg*
320 What Is Green? *by Mary O'Neill*

INFORMATIONAL ARTICLE

316 Desert Traders *by Iona S. Hiser*

SKILLS LESSONS

277 *Skill Lesson 5:* Making Mental Pictures
309 *Skill Lesson 6:* Recognizing the Power of Words

FUN AND GAMES

282 Commands *by Harriet Carlson*
346 *BIBLIOGRAPHY*
347 GLOSSARY
360 ARTIST CREDITS

Carousel

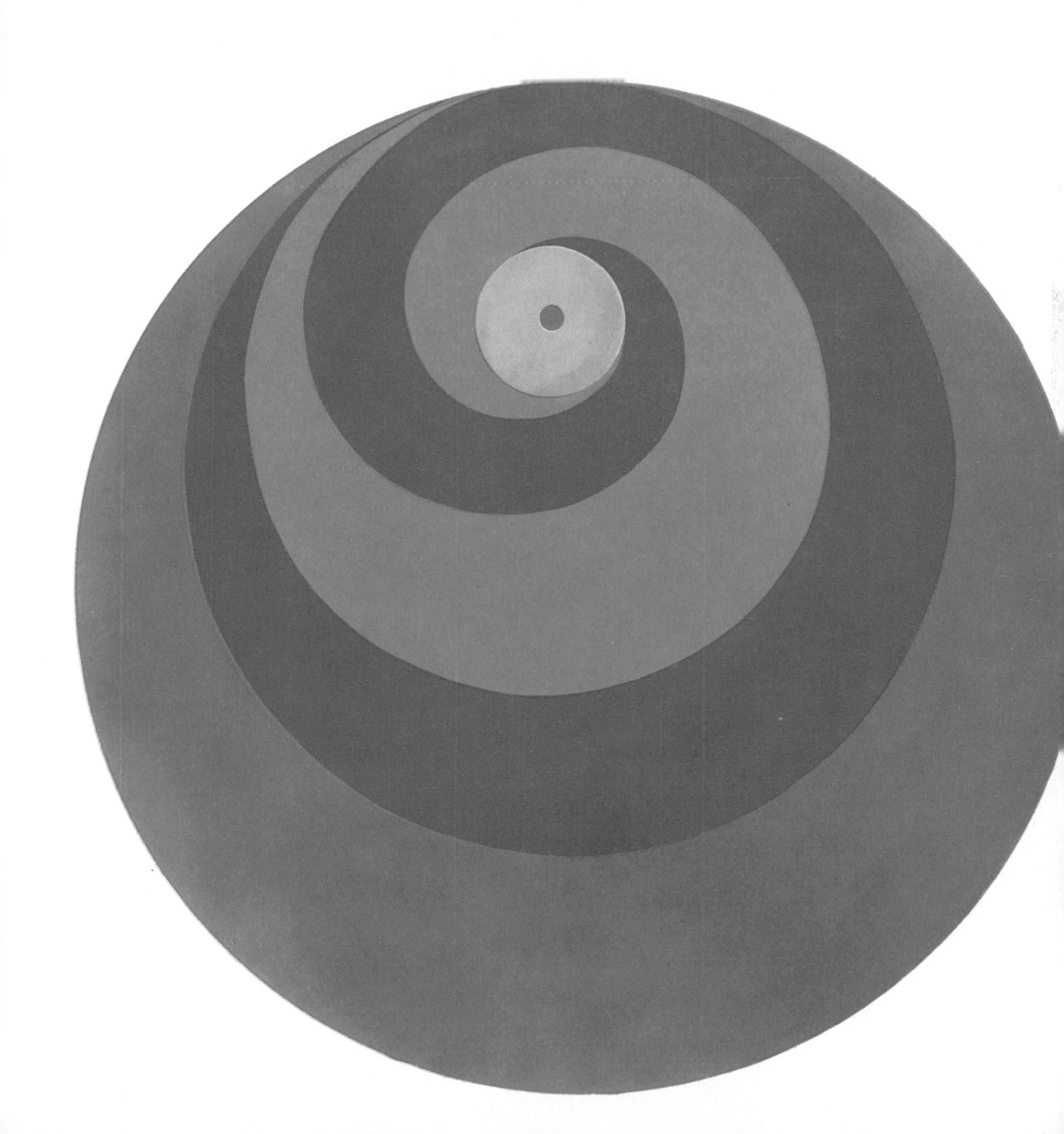

CAROUSEL

A VISIT TO THE MAYOR 9
by Nellie Burchardt

AUTUMN THOUGHT 27
by Langston Hughes

DOCTORING AN ELEPHANT 28
by William Bridges

GOLDFISH 40
by Kaye Starbird

RONNIE AND THE ADMIRAL 42
by Jack Bechdolt

IN THE FOG 60
by Lilian Moore

Skill Lesson 1: RECOGNIZING AND UNDERSTANDING SIMILES 61

FATS, THE BIG OPERATOR 66
by Marion Holland

BEWARE, MY CHILD 81
by Shel Silverstein

BEFORE YOU SPEND THAT COIN . . . 82
by Eva Knox Evans

Skill Lesson 2: RECOGNIZING AND UNDERSTANDING METAPHORS 90

THE PROBLEM 95
by Kaye Starbird

A Story Treasure from PAUL BUNYAN SWINGS HIS AXE 96
by Dell J. McCormick

BIBLIOGRAPHY 108

A VISIT TO THE MAYOR

BY NELLIE BURCHARDT

Betsy and her friend Ellen were worried. They had found a stray cat in the City Housing Project. The cat was about to have kittens, and the weather was getting cold outside. Betsy wanted very much to take the cat as her pet. But there was a rule against keeping pets in the Project.

As they walked up the hill to the store, Betsy suddenly exclaimed, "I've got it!"

"What've you got?" asked Ellen.

"How we can get the Project people to change the rule about pets."

"How?"

"Remember last month your mother and my mother were getting people to sign a petition for more crossing guards on the street? Why couldn't we get up a petition about pets and ask everyone in the Project to sign it?"

"Who would we give it to?" asked Ellen.

"The mayor. I saw a picture of him in the paper yesterday with his dog. If he can have a pet, how come we can't?"

Ellen looked thoughtful. "Do you really think it would work?"

"I don't know, but it's worth trying," said Betsy. "Can you think of any better way to get the rule changed?"

"No."

"Then let's write out the petition as soon as we get back. We can make enough copies for the other kids, and they can help us take them around to all the buildings," said Betsy.

Getting the Signatures

The petition drew smiles and wishes of good luck from most of the people the children asked to sign it. When Betsy rang the first few door-bells, her hands were cold with nervousness. The paper shook when she held it out to be signed. But most of the tenants seemed friendly, and soon she felt at ease.

The old man who answered her next bell could not find his glasses, so Betsy had to read the petition out loud to him. Part of the request had been copied from her mother's petition.

"Mr. Mayor," Betsy read from the paper. "We, the undersigned tenants of the City Housing Project, do respectfully request that the rule against pets in the City Housing Project be changed. Is it fair, Mr. Mayor, for you to have a dog when we are not allowed to have pets of any kind in the Project?"

The old man smiled.

"You're absolutely right, girls," the old man said. "I've often wished I could have a cat myself. And

I'll tell you a secret. There's a stray cat down in the bushes that somebody has been feeding." His eyes twinkled.

Betsy and Ellen looked at each other. Ellen burst into giggles. "We're the ones!" she shrieked.

"So that's it!" said the man. "I thought she was looking a lot better lately. Well, of course I'll have to sign your petition then." He signed his name at the end of the list. "How many signatures do you have now?"

"With yours, that makes eighty-seven. But our friends are getting signatures, too."

They had all agreed to meet at Betsy's apartment just before supper. When they counted up all the signatures, they found that they had four hundred and nineteen.

"That ought to be enough," said Betsy. "Tomorrow, right after school, we can take the petition to City Hall."

When word got around that they were going to the Mayor's office, almost all the children who had ever watched the cat being fed turned up at Betsy's apartment. She was stunned at the size of the group.

"Well," she said. "I guess the more we have, the more impressed the mayor will be."

Miss Witherspoon

"Now let's all be quiet," said Betsy when they arrived at City Hall. "They'll never let us see the mayor if we make a lot of noise."

The children climbed the steps of the huge stone building. Down the long marble hallway to the mayor's office they walked. The sound of their footsteps was lost in the great, high-ceilinged hall.

As they approached the mayor's office, the other children held back more and more, leaving Betsy in front.

"Please, Miss," she said to the lady at the desk by the door that said MAYOR. "We'd like to see the mayor."

"Do you have an appointment?" asked the lady, looking up from her desk.

"No. We didn't know you had to. But we have a petition for him."

The lady held out her hand. "I'll take care of it. You needn't wait," she said.

The children looked at each other doubtfully. Ellen shook her head at Betsy but didn't say anything.

"No," said Betsy. "We want to see the mayor in person."

CITY HALL
259

"I'm sorry, but the mayor is very busy at a City Council meeting."

The children eyed each other again.

"We'll wait," said Betsy.

"I said the mayor is very busy," said the lady, beginning to sound annoyed. "You can't see him now."

"That's all right, Miss. We have lots of time," said Betsy. "We'll sit down and wait till he's not busy." She turned and led the way to a bench against the wall. The other children followed her and sat down in a row on the bench.

The lady at the desk pushed back her chair and stood up. "Now, listen here, all of you," she said. "I told you that you *can't* wait. The mayor is too busy to have a bunch of noisy kids hanging around the office."

The lady seemed quite angry. Betsy wished the other children would not leave all the talking to her.

"We'll be very quiet, Miss. Please — we just *have* to see him," she pleaded. "It's very important."

She started to get up, but hesitated when she saw a door open behind the lady's back. A tall, rather stout man stood in the doorway. In the

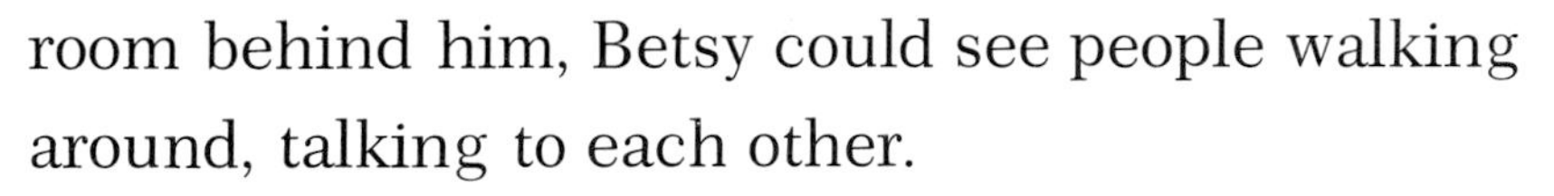

room behind him, Betsy could see people walking around, talking to each other.

The lady did not see the man. She walked toward the children with her arm raised, pointing at the door down the hall where they had come in.

"I said NO! Now, out with you!" she said.

"Come, come, Miss Witherspoon," said the man. "That's no way to treat a group of future voters."

Miss Witherspoon spun around. "Oh — Mr. Mayor!" she gasped. "I didn't realize you were there. I'm so sorry if we disturbed you. I — I — I was just trying to persuade these children to leave, but they absolutely refuse to."

"Have you tried twisting their arms?" asked the mayor, with a wink at the children.

"Twisting their arms!" exclaimed Miss Witherspoon in a horrified voice. Then she giggled. "Oh — you're joking again. I just never know when you're joking."

"But I'm glad you didn't persuade them to leave," continued the mayor. "It's not every day that I get a chance to talk to a group of my younger constituents."

The children exchanged puzzled looks.

"Now don't tell me that you didn't know you were my constituents," said the mayor.

The children shook their heads.

"Well, don't let it worry you. It just means you're the people I represent. You know what that means, don't you?"

The children nodded their heads.

"Now," said the mayor. "Out with it. To what do I owe the honor of this visit?"

Betsy Explains

Ellen gave Betsy a shove, and Betsy had to take a step forward to keep her balance.

"Yes?" said the mayor.

When he looked at her, her stomach felt shaky. He had not seemed so enormous in the picture she had seen in the paper.

"We — we — we have a petition here for you, M-Mr. Mayor," stuttered Betsy. She was surprised to hear how little and shaky her voice sounded. She handed him the papers covered with signatures.

The mayor took the papers from Betsy with one hand, and with the other he reached into his pocket and pulled out his glasses. He adjusted them on his nose and read the petition. Then he turned the pages of signatures one by one and examined them carefully.

Finally he looked up at Betsy and said, "So I can have a pet and you can't, is that it?"

"Yes, sir," said Betsy in a tiny voice.

"And you don't think that's fair, eh?"

"N-n-no, sir."

"What kind of pet would you get if you could have one?" asked the mayor.

Betsy took a deep breath. "A cat. You see, there's this poor little cat that has a lame paw — "

Suddenly the other children found their voices, and all started speaking at once.

" — and we've been feeding her — "

" — and she's going to have kittens — "

" — but we're not allowed to have pets — "

" — and the weather's getting too cold — "

"Whoa! Whoa!" shouted the mayor over the babble of voices. "One at a time!"

The children fell silent.

Now that he could make himself heard, the mayor looked right at Betsy and said, "This seems to be something of an emergency. Is that it?"

"Yes, sir," said Betsy. "She's going to have her kittens any day now. And if she has them outside, she'll hide them somewhere, and we won't be able to find them before winter comes."

"You know what I'd like to do?" the mayor asked.

"N-no, sir." Betsy's voice was small and scared.

"I'd *like* to insist that you children take those kittens in and give them decent homes."

Betsy gave a sigh of relief.

"*But,*" continued the mayor, "there's only one catch."

Betsy and her friends exchanged worried looks.

"What's that?" asked Betsy.

"I don't make the rules. The City Council has to approve any change in the rules for the Project. You know, you're not the first ones who have said the rule against pets was unfair. Now — I wonder what we could do about it." He was silent for a moment.

The children watched his face anxiously.

"Hm-m-m — yes. It just might work," he said at last. He looked at Betsy. "What's your name, little girl?"

"Who? Me?" Betsy looked around, hoping he meant some other child.

"Yes — you."

"Oh. Betsy."

"All right, Betsy. Do you think you could go in there to the City Council meeting and show them the petition just the way you showed it to me?"

"Oh — no!" Betsy stepped back toward the protection of the rest of the group. "I'd be too scared."

"You weren't too scared of me, were you, Betsy?" asked the mayor.

"No-o-o." She remembered that she *had* been afraid of him. But that seemed a little silly now. He was not a bit fierce.

"Do you want to keep that cat, Betsy?" he asked.

"Oh — yes! I do!"

Betsy bit her lip. That cat was certainly leading her into doing a lot of things she would have been too scared to do last year — writing a petition, ringing all those strange doorbells to get signatures, talking to the mayor. And now he wanted her to face the City Council! Well, she'd come this far. She couldn't give up now.

"All right. I *guess* I could do it," she said.

"That's the girl!" exclaimed the mayor.

A Very Determined Young Lady

As Betsy and the mayor entered the room, the council members went back to their seats. Betsy almost changed her mind when she saw all those strange grown-up faces staring at her from around the big council-room table. The council members looked like the kind of people who could say "No" to almost anything.

The mayor sat down in the chair at the head of the table and told her to stand beside him. He rapped on the table for silence.

"I'd like to make a change in the order of business," he said. "I want to introduce a very determined young lady to you. Her name is Betsy — uh —Betsy, what's your last name?"

"Delaney."

"Her name is Betsy Delaney, and she has a problem for you."

To be called "determined" made Betsy feel a little braver. She tried not to think of all those grown-up eyes looking at her. She tried to think instead of the cat's green-and-gold eyes.

Once she started talking, it was not as hard as she had thought it would be to explain about the petition and the lame cat the children had been feeding. When she had finished and had passed around the petition for all of them to examine, the mayor motioned to her to lean closer to him.

He whispered in her ear, "This isn't a promise, Betsy, but if I were you, I'd go home and catch that cat and lock her up before she starts having kittens all over the place."

Betsy grinned. "Oh, yes, sir!" she said.

As she turned to leave, she saw the mayor very distinctly wink at her. She winked back. It

seemed silly now that she had been so scared of him at first.

The newspaper lay on the hall floor just outside the door to Betsy's apartment when she came home from school the next day. Betsy snatched it up. She searched through it until she found a short paragraph at the bottom of the fifth page.

"CITY COUNCIL CHANGES RULE TO ALLOW PETS IN HOUSING PROJECT," it started.

AUTHOR

"A Visit to the Mayor" is from Nellie Burchardt's popular book, *Project Cat.* Mrs. Burchardt lives on Staten Island, New York, and enjoys writing about city children. She once worked as a librarian in New York City but is now a housewife and the mother of two daughters.

Mrs. Burchardt likes to think of stories while she is doing her housework. She says, "It blocks out my 'I don't want to do dishes' thoughts." When she sits down for lunch, she writes out her ideas so she won't forget them. Mrs. Burchardt then tries out her stories on her own children. She feels that they are good judges of what other young people will like to read and says they often make useful suggestions.

Besides *Project Cat,* you will also enjoy reading *Reggie's No-Good Bird,* another book about a city housing project.

Autumn Thought

Flowers are happy in summer.
In autumn they die and are blown away.
   Dry and withered,
Their petals dance on the wind
Like little brown butterflies.

– *Langston Hughes*

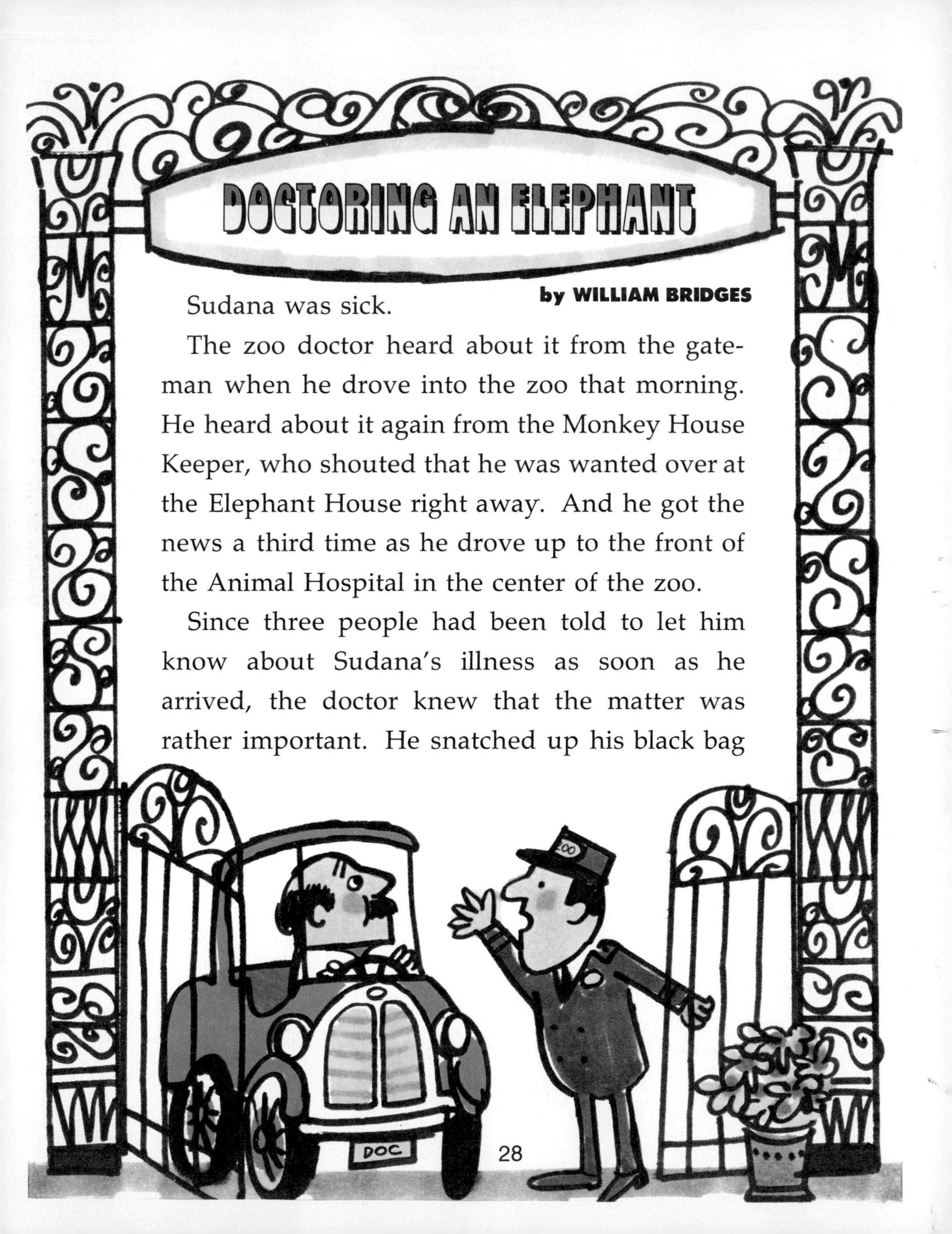

DOCTORING AN ELEPHANT

by WILLIAM BRIDGES

Sudana was sick.

The zoo doctor heard about it from the gateman when he drove into the zoo that morning. He heard about it again from the Monkey House Keeper, who shouted that he was wanted over at the Elephant House right away. And he got the news a third time as he drove up to the front of the Animal Hospital in the center of the zoo.

Since three people had been told to let him know about Sudana's illness as soon as he arrived, the doctor knew that the matter was rather important. He snatched up his black bag

of emergency medicines. Then he hurried out to the animal ambulance and roared away.

Bob, the Elephant House Keeper, came out to meet him as he drew up at the front door. "I'm glad you're here, Doc. Sudana's mighty sick."

"When did all this happen?"

"In the night, I guess. Last evening I left her food and water. She hardly ate anything in the night, and this morning she kept acting as if she wanted water. I filled the trough twice and she kept begging for more, but I was afraid to give her too much. And she feels all hot."

"Hmm. Let's have a look."

Sudana certainly did look sick. The big African elephant was leaning against the steel bars at the front of the Elephant House.

"What's the matter, old girl? This isn't like you, Sudana." The doctor talked soothingly while he slowly climbed over the guardrail and reached through the bars to lay a hand on the elephant's trunk. He felt it in several places and then slipped his hand under her ear and down the length of her foreleg and back along her body. Sudana had a fever, and it was a high one.

"Don't give her any more water. We've got to

get some medicine into her, and she isn't going to like the taste of it. But if she's thirsty enough, maybe she'll take it in her drinking water." The doctor watched Sudana thoughtfully for a few minutes. It was important to figure out her weight carefully, in order to know how much medicine powder to give her.

Eight thousand pounds, more or less, was what Sudana must weigh now. That meant about four cupfuls of sulfadiazine that he'd have to get into Sudana somehow. The doctor drove back to the hospital in the ambulance.

He said to the nurse, "Weigh out four hundred and eighty grams of sulfadiazine and put it into three packages."

"Four hundred and eighty grams? Why, that's enough for an elephant!"

"It *is* for an elephant — Sudana," said the doctor.

At noon he was back at the Elephant House. Sudana looked even sicker and more woebegone than she had before.

"This has been a rough morning, Doc," said Bob. "She keeps feeling the water trough with her trunk, and then she looks at me, and I can hardly stand it."

"You didn't give her any, did you?"

"Not a drop," said Bob.

"I know it's hard on you and on Sudana, too. But she's a mighty sick elephant, and this is the surest way I know to get that medicine down her. Now you run her into the next stall, so she can't see me while I mix the medicine with her drinking water."

The doctor slit open one package of the white powder and poured it into Sudana's drinking trough. He mixed it with the water. "We'll have to give her the dose in three parts. I'm a little afraid she'll taste it even like this. She certainly would if we dumped in the whole dose at once."

Sudana smelled the water. She headed straight for her trough and drew up a couple of gallons through her trunk.

Suddenly Sudana's trunk jerked out of her mouth. She aimed her trunk at the doctor and her keeper. They ducked, but it was too late. The cold sulfadiazine-and-water mixture hit them straight in their faces.

"Serves me right for tricking her!" thought Bob.

"So *that* didn't work!" the doctor was thinking. "Now what do we do?"

While they cleaned up, the doctor said, "Sudana likes ice cream, doesn't she?"

"She's crazy about it. People give her ice-cream cones and she never gets enough."

"Well, we might try giving her ice cream," said the doctor. "Here's how we'll work it. I'll mix her medicine in a quart of ice cream. She won't trust you and me. We tricked her with that water, and she'll remember it. But I'll have Jim come over and feed her the stuff in ice-cream cones!"

Bob smiled. "That'll do the trick, Doc! You send Jim over. I'll stay out of sight."

Back at the hospital, the doctor ordered a quart of chocolate ice cream and a box of cones. "Change into your street clothes," he told Jim, his hospital helper. "I want you to stand around in the crowd, like any visitor, and offer these cones to Sudana. As far as she'll know, you'll be just another visitor with something good to eat."

First the doctor set aside enough plain ice cream to fill two of the cones. Then he mixed a full dose of sulfadiazine into the rest of the ice cream. He put all the cones into a box, with the ones without any medicine on top.

"She's a smart elephant and you'll have to outsmart her," the doctor told Jim. "Walk over to the Elephant House and wait until you see people feeding the elephants. Then hold out one of these two cones on the top. Let Sudana have both of them. They don't have any medicine, so she'll swallow them and reach for more. Then give her the medicated ones as fast you can get her to take them."

"Sounds easy enough," said Jim.

The doctor telephoned the Elephant House. "Jim's on his way. This time I think we'll fool her."

In five minutes Jim was back. The front of his shirt and most of his coat were dripping with melted chocolate ice cream and sulfadiazine!

Just in Time

There was only one thing left to do: give Sudana a whopping big shot of penicillin! It had to be done, one way or another.

Bob was doubtful. "That's a long time for an elephant to hold still. I could try feeding her apples. That's a treat she doesn't get very often. Is the shot going to hurt her?"

"Not really. Not as much as it would hurt you or me."

The doctor was sure that Bob could handle her. He was a good keeper. Bob got a bucket of apples while the doctor prepared the needle with the penicillin.

"I'm ready, Bob. Start feeding her."

Bob set the bucket down in front of Sudana. "Steady, girl! Apples, Sudana! Steady now!" Bob held an apple so her trunk could curl around it, and swiftly she tucked it into her mouth.

"All right, Doc."

Sudana was reaching for another apple when the doctor stepped between the bars. One eye rolled in his direction, but she made no move.

"Don't talk to her, Doc. Just do your stuff and get out as fast as you can. I've got her steady."

The doctor pinched the gray skin under the foreleg into a broad fold and plunged the needle as deep as it would go.

Sudana flinched.

"Steady, Sudana! Steady, girl. Here's another apple. Steady, now." Bob's voice was calm and soothing. Sudana's trunk dipped into the bucket, rose to her mouth, and dipped into the bucket again.

"We're still all right, Doc, but you'd better hurry. I can see the bottom of the bucket."

Finally it was done! With a quick tug, the doctor pulled the needle out.

"Just in time, Doc," said Bob as he stood up, spilling the last two apples on the floor. "Did you give her the full dose?"

"Yes. I think she'll be all right. Her fever ought to come down tonight. Give her a light feeding and all the water she wants. She ought to be OK in a few days."

She was.

AUTHOR

The author of "Doctoring an Elephant," William Bridges, worked for many years as a newspaper reporter. After spending several years working for American newspapers in France, he returned to New York. There he first wrote newspaper articles about the animals in the Bronx Zoo. Then he was hired by the Zoo itself and placed in charge of all its written material. Mr. Bridges has been sent to many different countries as part of his interesting job.

The story of Sudana is a chapter from his book, *Zoo Doctor.* Mr. Bridges has written several other books about zoo animals, such as *Zoo Babies, Zoo Pets,* and *Zoo Expeditions.*

I MATSUMOTO

GOLDFISH

I wonder about the thoughts and goals
Of goldfish living in goldfish bowls.

A goldfish drifts through his fishbowl greenery
And never mentions the lovely scenery
Or says he's really enthusiastic
About his pebbles of gay green plastic.

He never raves, with his fish-eyes glowing,
About the places he plans on going.

Of course, he probably finds it hard
(Forever circling his liquid yard)
To know the spot where his trips begin
And whether he's going or he's been.

But even when told Which Way Is West,
A goldfish *still* doesn't seem impressed.

You tell a goldfish the time of day
Or what he's having for dinner, say,
Or what the weather prediction is
And see if you get a glad "Gee whiz!"

You're lucky to get, for all your trouble,
A passing comment of one small bubble.

– *Kaye Starbird*

RONNIE and the ADMIRAL

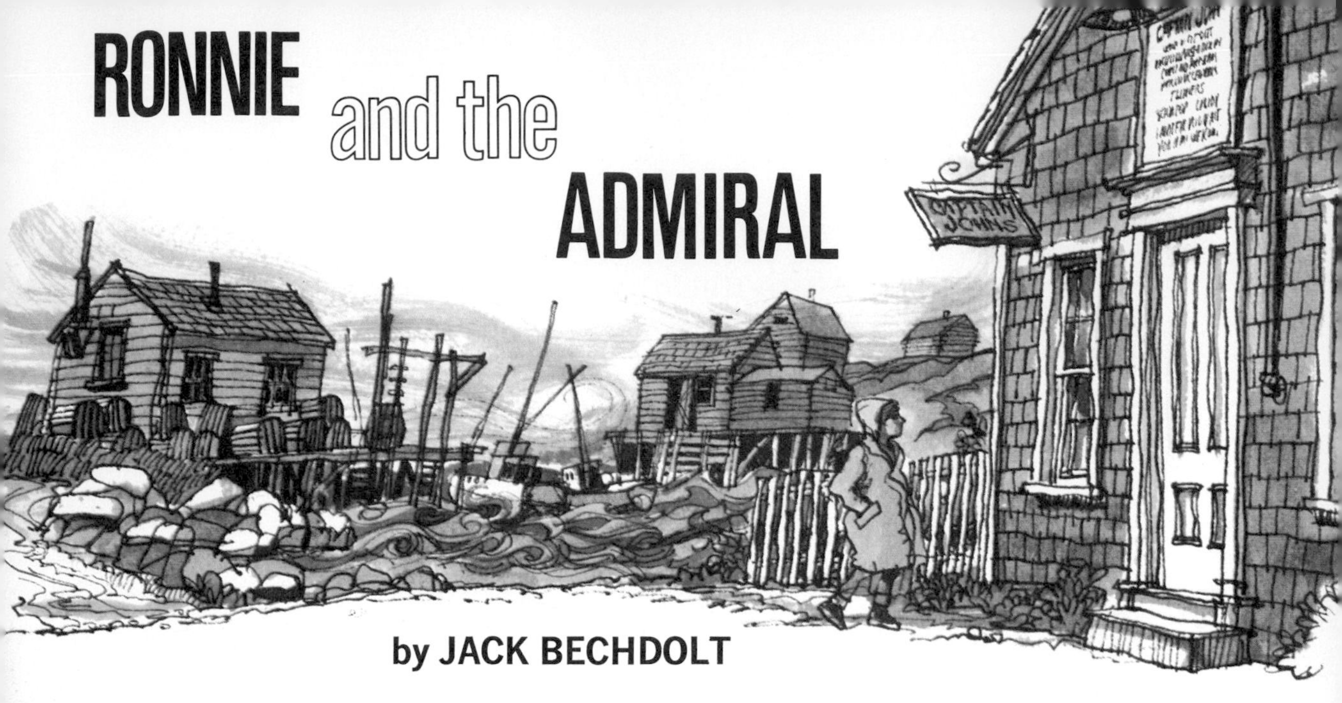

by JACK BECHDOLT

A northeast storm was lashing Sandy Bay Village the day Ronnie Spicer entered Captain John's shop.

A sign over the door said:

When Ronnie opened the door, a bell tinkled. A hearty voice bellowed, "Steady as she goes. I'll be with you in a minute."

Ronnie looked around. The room was filled with many things for sale. There were stacks of straw hats, fishing gear, baskets of vegetables, tin cans filled with flowers, penny candies, a few groceries, and a sign that said:

Beyond the shop was a kitchen. The door stood open, and Ronnie saw someone bending over a steaming pot. A delicious smell of clam juice, hot milk, and onions filled the air. A table was spread with a red and white checked cloth. The man was Captain John.

"Haul alongside, lad," he said. "Chowder's almost ready."

"I didn't come for chowder," Ronnie began. "I — I was just looking around. I'm afraid I haven't any money to spend."

"Money?" bellowed the Captain. "Who said anything about money? The Admiral and I want your company, don't we, Admiral?"

Ronnie glanced around for the person the captain was talking to. He saw no one.

Then just behind him a hoarse voice muttered, "Slit his gizzard . . . slit his gizzard!" The words were followed by a gasp and then a shriek of mad laughter.

Something whizzed past Ronnie's head. He leaped aside with a cry. Then suddenly he felt rather silly.

The speaker was a parrot. The bird had landed on the kitchen table and was swaggering back

and forth, spreading his feathers and chuckling. He rolled wicked eyes at Ronnie.

"Blow the swab down," he muttered.

"Well!" said Ronnie. He tried to laugh, but found himself a little out of breath.

"Don't you mind the Admiral," Captain John laughed. "Poor old Admiral Benbow!"

The bird hunched his shoulders and dragged his wings. "Poor old Admiral Benbow," he squawked. Ronnie laughed aloud.

"He's taken a fancy to you," said Captain John. "Not many people he likes."

Ronnie offered the Admiral a bite of cracker. The Admiral ate it, cocked his head on one side, and murmured gently, "Cut your throat? Cut your throat for a nickel, you swab!"

"He doesn't mean a word of it," Captain John explained. "He talks that way because he spent his youth in bad company."

During the long summer vacation that followed, Ronnie saw the Captain and the Admiral often.

One morning in late summer, Ronnie found the Captain staring at a yellow telegram.

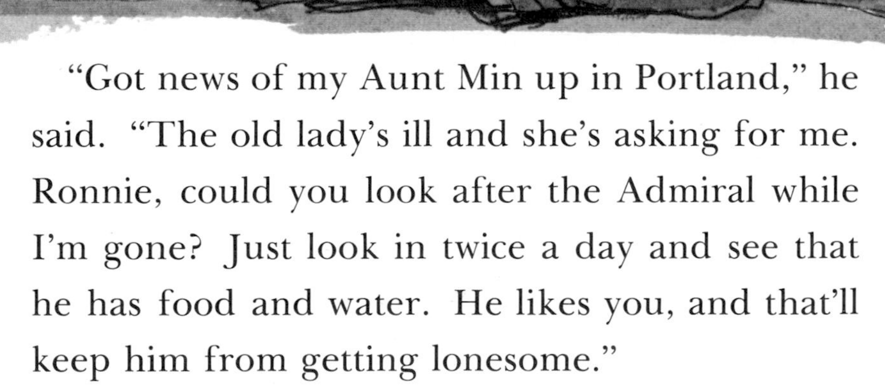

"Got news of my Aunt Min up in Portland," he said. "The old lady's ill and she's asking for me. Ronnie, could you look after the Admiral while I'm gone? Just look in twice a day and see that he has food and water. He likes you, and that'll keep him from getting lonesome."

"Of course I will," Ronnie agreed.

"I'll give you the key," the Captain explained. "Just let the old boy have the run of the shop daytimes. At night he ought to be put in his cage. It gets chilly at night, and parrots get pneumonia easily. All you have to do is pop him in and cover the cage with that big black cloth I keep handy. That helps shut out the cold air. You won't have any trouble. He trusts you."

"Why, it won't be any trouble at all," Ronnie said. "We're friends."

Captain John put up the heavy shutters and nailed a sign on the door:

CLOSED FOR SEASON

Ronnie began his chores as watchman and caretaker of the parrot that evening. He made sure the doors and windows were locked. Then he unfolded the big black cloth that the captain used to cover the cage.

"Come on, Admiral. Time to pipe down!"

"Awrrk," said the Admiral and hopped out of reach. Every time Ronnie came a step nearer, he hopped again.

"This won't do," thought Ronnie. He pretended not to notice the parrot by turning his back and whistling a tune.

The Admiral perched on the counter and dozed. Ronnie made a sudden pounce. He had him. The black cloth wound around the bird. Ronnie started toward the cage, which hung in the window.

The cloth was jumping and twisting as the Admiral struggled. Ronnie could hardly hold onto it. The Admiral's beak closed over his thumb and sank deep. Frantic claws dug into his arm. Ronnie let go and the cloth flew open. Admiral Benbow burst out, shrieking. He circled Ronnie's head, beating his wings at him, and then fled to the highest crossbeam.

Ronnie's thumb had been bitten badly. He had to take care of the cut. The parrot watched from above.

"You're going into that cage, like it or not," Ronnie cried as he searched for the medicine bottle. "You're not going to catch cold and die of pneumonia if I can help it."

He dragged a table to a spot just beneath the Admiral's perch. He set a kitchen chair on its top.

He climbed carefully up on the chair. The parrot was screaming. Ronnie grabbed the parrot with the black cloth. Now he had him! The beating wings were tangled in the cloth. He made a quick reach to pull the Admiral off his perch. The kitchen chair rocked. When Ronnie tried to get his balance, the Admiral got out of the cloth and flew down upon him.

Ronnie jumped down. The Admiral returned to his roost.

"You'll just have to stay there for the night, you old fool," Ronnie said. But that night he worried. What if the Admiral did get pneumonia?

In spite of Ronnie's fears, the bird was fine when Ronnie visited him next morning. The Admiral fluttered down and perched on Ronnie's shoulder. He murmured lovingly, "Cut your throat?"

"I'd like to cut yours," Ronnie snapped.

Ronnie could not persuade the Admiral to get into his cage, so he built a small fire. That sent the warm air up among the beams where the Admiral had chosen to roost.

The next night a heavy fog swept in from the sea. It was dark and cold when Ronnie came to the shop. There were no sounds except the whisper of waves on the sand and the "hoo-hoot" of a distant foghorn.

An old blue car was standing near the shop with its motor running. It had out-of-state license plates, and its back seat was piled high with bundles.

"Somebody on his way home after summer vacation," Ronnie thought.

A Wise Old Bird

He opened the front door of Captain John's shop and called, "Ahoy, Admiral!"

There was no answer.

Behind Ronnie the shop door blew shut with a loud bang that made him jump. He felt along the shelf behind the counter for a box of matches and a lamp he kept handy there.

A board creaked. Then another! Somebody, or something, was stirring in the shop.

"Where did I put that lamp?" he wondered. The floor creaked again.

"Hey, Admiral!" Ronnie called.

"Shut up," said a hoarse voice at his ear. It was not the voice of the Admiral. At the same time a heavy hand was clamped across his mouth. On either side of him a man pressed close.

"Listen, and get this right," said the hoarse voice. "You won't get hurt if you do what you're told. Understand?"

Ronnie managed to nod.

These men were thieves! That must be their car he had seen waiting outside.

"Light that lamp. The windows are shuttered. Nobody's going to see it," said the hoarse-voiced man.

The hand was removed from Ronnie's mouth. The thief turned to the lamp on the counter. The other turned his flashlight on Ronnie, half blinding him.

"Not a move!" he said. "Not one squawk, and if you're spoken to, you give straight answers, understand?"

Again Ronnie nodded. The flame from the lamp spread a soft glow about them. The hoarse-voiced man leaned forward until his face nearly touched Ronnie's.

"Now, you, what are you doing here?"

"I — I work here," Ronnie stuttered.

"Oh, so you work here. Kind of a watchman, eh?" The two men exchanged glances.

"Get that, Nate?" said Hoarse Voice. "The kid's going to be real useful to us."

The taller man grinned. "Let me talk to him. I've got a way with kids."

"Now, Sonny," said Nate. "You listen to me. You don't want to get hurt, do you? All right then," Nate whispered on. "All you've got to do is answer a question — *and answer it true*! Where does the old man keep his money?"

"I don't know," Ronnie gasped. "Honestly I don't!"

"Oh, you don't know!" Nate snarled. "You just think again."

"But I don't! Please, you must believe me, I don't know!"

Hoarse Voice said, "Maybe he don't. It could be."

"Oh, yeah?" said Nate. "He's lying." He bent closer to Ronnie, grabbed the boy's arm, and twisted. Ronnie cried out with the pain.

"Now," said Nate softly. "You think it over. Where does the old man keep his money?"

"I don't know," Ronnie repeated. "It's the truth."

Nate's fingers dug into Ronnie's arm. "Talk fast — ," he was whispering. "You'd better talk fast, before —"

"Slit his gizzard," said another speaker. "Slit his gizzard."

Nate let go of the arm and whirled around. "Who's that? Quick, put out that light!"

The hoarse-voiced man blew out the lamp flame. The strange voice began to mutter again. It sounded like the voices of several men muttering to each other.

"What are we waiting for?" Nate snarled. "Get out the back window before they find us."

Ronnie's heart was hammering. The thieves were groping their way toward the rear of the shop where they had broken in.

"Help!" Ronnie shouted. "Help! Thieves!"

Instantly he wished he had kept still. The sound of Ronnie's voice started the Admiral on a tirade of babbling, squawking, and shrieking.

"Slit his gizzard — cut his throat — blow the swab down . . . awrk-awrk-awrk!"

"Hey, what's all this?" Hoarse Voice shouted. "Give me that flashlight!"

The beam of the flashlight rested on the little candy counter. There stood Admiral Benbow, wings flapping, shrieking with laughter.

"A parrot!" Hoarse Voice growled. "Just a stupid parrot, and you thought it was the police! That's one on you, Nate."

"Cut your throat for a nickel?" cooed Admiral Benbow.

"Aw, light that lamp again and let's get finished," Nate snapped. "Say, wait! We can take that parrot along. That's a valuable bird, and I know where we can get a good price for him."

"Go driving across the country with a fool parrot yelling his head off? Attracting the attention of every policeman we pass? You're crazy!"

"He won't scream his head off. There's his cage. Put him in it and cover him up. A parrot won't talk if you cover his cage." Nate turned to Ronnie. "Right?"

"Yes sir," Ronnie agreed. "That's how the Captain keeps him quiet."

He wondered if Nate noticed that his voice was shaking. "He — the Captain — he just throws that black cloth that's on the counter over the cage and — the Admiral pipes down."

"There, you see!" Nate exclaimed. He snatched up the cloth, shook out its folds, and waved it to the Admiral. "Pretty Poll," he cooed. "Pretty Poll, come here, Polly!"

The Admiral came, giving a wild shriek. As he swooped past Nate's head, he clawed Nate's cheek.

"Get him off!" Nate roared. He was frantically clutching his cheek as he staggered into a shelf of chinaware. The shelf gave way, and china crashed to the floor. The hoarse-voiced thief fell as he turned and made for the door. Admiral Benbow took time out to swoop down upon him and bite his ear.

It was at that point that Ronnie hurried out of the shop. When he returned with the sheriff and several neighbors, the two thieves were gone. Perched upon the wreckage of overturned chairs and broken china was Admiral Benbow.

"Don't worry, Ronnie," said the sheriff. "My men will catch them. They can't get too far in that old car. You really did some quick thinking when you got the license number."

"And to think," cried Ronnie, "if I'd had my way, that parrot would have been shut up in his cage where he couldn't do anything to help me. Admiral, you're a wise old bird!"

Admiral Benbow fluttered to Ronnie's shoulder, where he could rub lovingly against Ronnie's cheek.

"Cut your throat?" he cooed. "Cut your throat for a nickel, you swab?"

AUTHOR

Jack Bechdolt was born in Minnesota in 1884. When he was a young boy, he had a back injury and had to spend several months strapped to a board. His family claims that this was the reason he grew so tall and thin!

Mr. Bechdolt was working as a newspaperman when he became interested in writing stories for young people. He began to sell his stories to magazines and then wrote some books for young people. His wife, Decie Merwin, was also a writer, and together they wrote many more books. Most of these books are now out of print, but you may still be able to find some of them in your library. Mr. Bechdolt and his wife together wrote the *Dulcie* series (*Dulcie and Her Donkey* and others), *John's Dragon,* and *Roscoe.* Mr. Bechdolt also wrote *Going Up, Little Boy with a Big Horn,* and *Horse Stories.* He died in 1954 at the age of 70.

IN THE FOG

Stand still.
The fog wraps you up
and no one can find you.
Walk.
The fog opens up
to let you through
and closes behind you.

– Lilian Moore

Skill Lesson 1:

RECOGNIZING AND UNDERSTANDING SIMILES

Suppose you wanted to tell someone what a fast runner a friend of yours is. Here are two sentences that you might use:

1. Joe can run faster than anyone else I know.
2. Joe can run as fast as a deer.

Each of those sentences says that Joe is a fast runner. Sentence 1 compares Joe with other people. It says that Joe can run faster than other people. Sentence 2 also compares Joe with something else, but it compares him with a deer instead of comparing him with people.

When we compare things that are *alike* in most ways, we are making a **simple comparison.** In Sentence 1, Joe, who is a person, is compared with other persons.

Since all persons are alike in most ways, the comparison between Joe and other persons is a simple comparison.

In Sentence 2, however, the comparison is between a person and a deer. Here the comparison is between things that are not alike. A comparison between quite *different* things is called a **simile** (sim′uh-lee).

Here are more examples of similes:

3. Mother was as busy as a bee.
4. That girl is slower than a turtle.
5. Bill ate his lunch like a starved bear.
6. Ralph jumped over the fence like a grasshopper.

Notice that in Sentence 3 the word *as* is used in making the comparison. In Sentence 4, the word *than* is used. In Sentences 5 and 6, the word *like* is used. When you see two things compared by using the words *as, than,* or *like* in your reading, remember that you may be reading a simile.

When a writer wants to make such things as the speed or size of something stand out very clearly, he very often uses a simile. That's because, in a simile, the *one* way in which the two things are alike stands out in your mind. In a simple comparison, you might think of other ways in which the two things are alike. A simile makes a stronger comparison. Most people feel that similes are more interesting to read than simple comparisons. Certainly, a simile is more interesting than a simple statement like "Joe can run very fast."

Usually you will understand the meaning of a simile right away. If you don't, you can almost always figure out what the author is trying to tell you if you do these things:

A. Make sure you know what two things are being compared.
B. Think how those two things could be alike.
C. Choose the one way in which they are alike that will make the most sense in what you are reading.

See if you can do those three things now with the simile in each of the following sentences:

7. Jim's as lazy as an old dog lying in the sun.
8. Mary was as excited over her new dress as a dog would be over a new bone.
9. Jane can sing like a bird.
10. When Bill looked out the airplane window, the cars and trucks below looked like toys.

Discussion

Help your class answer these questions:

1. What is the difference between a simple comparison and a simile?

2. Why do you think Joe was compared with a deer instead of a donkey?
3. What three words often show that a simile is being used?
4. Why do story writers often use similes?
5. What three things can you do to help you figure out the meaning of a simile?
6. In each of Sentences 3 through 10, what two things are being compared? How are those two things alike? What is the one likeness that the writer of each sentence was trying to tell you about?

On your own

Find the simile in each paragraph that follows. Then figure out what the speaker was trying to tell you by using that simile.

"John, your room is like a jungle," said Mr. Smith to his son. "I could hardly walk through to close the window this morning. After school today, I want you to pick up your things and put them away."

Bob and his friends couldn't play outside because it was a cold, rainy day. All five of the boys went down into the basement in Bob's house to play. It wasn't long before Bob's mother came to the top of the stairs and called down, "Boys, you'll have to play quieter games. You're making as much racket as a pack of starved wolves."

One evening, Ann's mother and father let her stay up late to watch a special show on TV. The next morning, she just couldn't seem to get going. Even after she washed up, she still felt sleepy. She was late getting to the breakfast table, and she took twice as long as usual to eat her eggs. Her mother finally said, "Ann, if you don't stop moving like a snail, you'll never get to school on time. Whatever is the matter with you?"

Checking your work

Talk with your class about the similes in the three paragraphs above. Decide whether or not you think each simile was a good way for the speaker in that paragraph to get his or her idea across.

FATS, THE BIG OPERATOR

by Marion Holland

Fats went over to Billy's house one day with a face about a mile long. Billy took one look at Fats and asked, "What's the matter with you?"

"I just broke something of Ellen's," said Fats. Ellen was Fats's big sister. "And, oh brother, am I going to be in trouble when she gets home!"

"Huh, you think you've got trouble," said Billy. "Come on in and take a look at what *I've* got."

Fats walked in and looked. A little girl, about three years old, was sitting on the floor, crying quietly. She just sat there, hugging an old beat-up teddy bear that had one eye missing and the other eye dangling by a thread.

"Her name's Gloria," Billy went on, "and her mother and my mother have gone downtown shopping. I have to take care of her till they get back. It wasn't *my* idea," he added.

Fats looked at Gloria. "She doesn't seem to be giving you any trouble," he said.

"Yeah, but I'm supposed to amuse her, and she sure isn't amused," complained Billy. "When you stay with your kid brothers, what do you *do*?"

"I don't do anything," said Fats. "It's what *they* do. Sometimes I can stop them and sometimes I can't."

"What, for instance?" asked Billy.

"Oh, they slide down the stairs in the laundry basket. Or climb up on the dressers and jump down on the beds. Or tip over all the chairs to make a train."

Billy shook his head. "I don't think Gloria would like any of those things," he said. "And what's more my mother wouldn't."

"I want my MAMA!" wailed Gloria.

"That's all she's said, so far," remarked Billy.

"You ought to cheer her up," said Fats. "That bear doesn't look any too good. Maybe we could fix it up for her."

He went over to Gloria. "Poor bear," he said. "Look at his eyes. He sure needs new eyes, doesn't he?"

Gloria only hugged the bear tighter.

"So you let me take him, just for a minute," suggested Fats. "And I'll fix him some nice new eyes. Okay?"

Gloria thought this over. "Okay," she said, handing the bear to Fats.

"That's just dandy," said Billy, "except that we're fresh out of bear eyes."

"Bear eyes," explained Fats, "are buttons. Where does your mom keep buttons and stuff?"

Billy got his mother's sewing basket. Fats poked around in it and found a card of fancy glass buttons with black centers.

"Hot diggity!" exclaimed Fats. "Best bear eyes I ever saw."

Gloria put her thumb in her mouth. She watched anxiously while Fats cut off the dangling eye and sewed on two shiny new eyes.

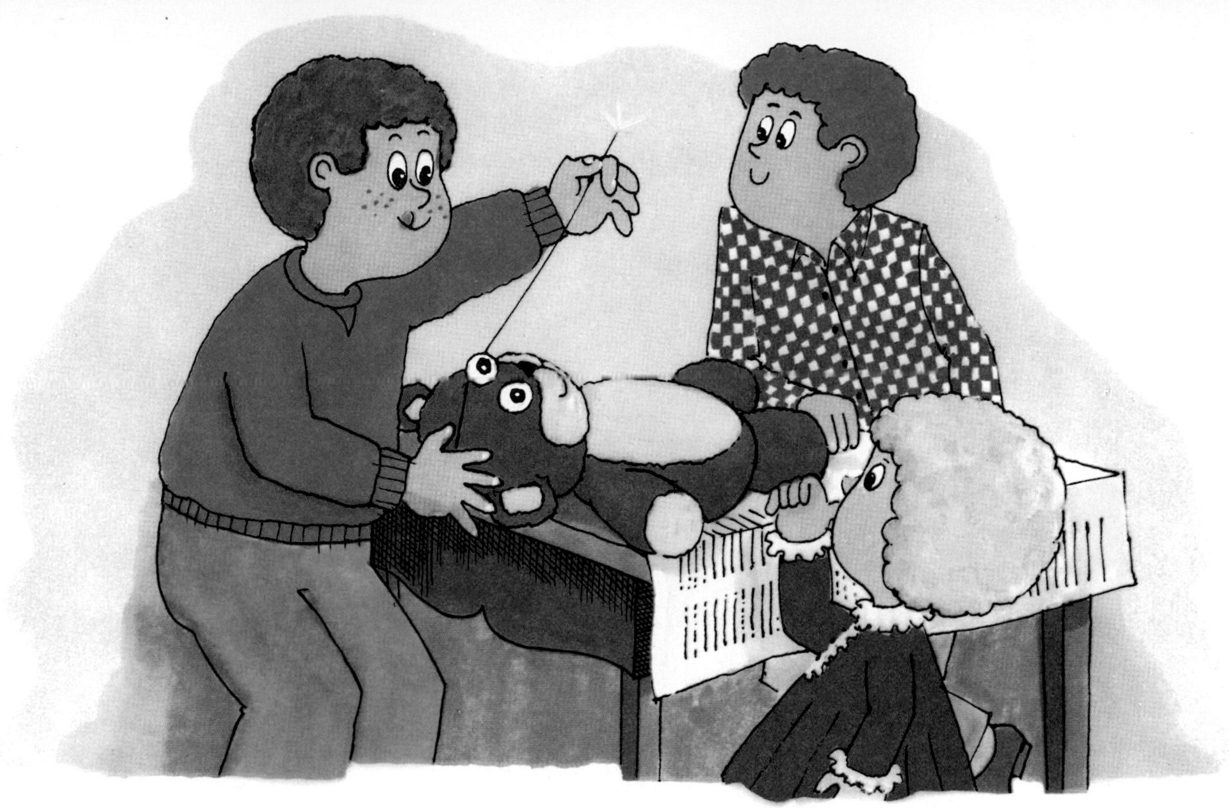

"There!" he said, biting off the thread. "Old Mr. Bear can see where he's going now, can't he?"

Gloria removed her thumb and smiled. Fats gave the bear a pat on the back. "Ow!" he exclaimed, shaking his hand. "What's this animal stuffed with, iron?" He prodded around its middle. "Say, there's something *in* this bear!"

"Let me see," said Billy, grabbing the bear. "Sure is heavy. It's some kind of machinery, I'll bet. Say, this bear is supposed to wind up and *do* something!"

Gloria opened her mouth wide and howled, "I want my *bear*!" Tears poured down her cheeks.

"Now look what you've done," said Fats. "And just when I had her all cheered up, too." He took the bear away from Billy and handed it to Gloria.

"I sure would like to get a look at whatever's inside that bear," said Billy. "I'll bet we could oil it up and make it work."

"Well, I'll see what I can do about it," said Fats. "Poor old bear," he said to Gloria. "He's sick. He feels terrible."

Gloria looked alarmed.

"But I'm the doctor, see?" Fats went on soothingly. "I can make him all well again."

Gloria looked unconvinced.

"Look at his nice new eyes. I fixed them fine, didn't I?"

Gloria nodded.

"Now I'm going to fix his insides, so he feels all better. Okay?"

"Okay," said Gloria reluctantly, holding out the bear.

"That's a good girl. Now you sit here and watch, but you must be very quiet. Understand?" Fats cleared some magazines off the table and spread out a newspaper and laid the bear on it.

"Operating table," he explained. Then he examined the patient. "There's a seam right down the middle of the back. I can just cut the stitches. Scissors won't do, though. Find a razor blade and an oil can. And a screwdriver and a flashlight, too."

"And just who do you think you're ordering around, anyway?" asked Billy.

"If I'm going to perform this operation, I need an assistant," said Fats coldly. "I've got troubles enough of my own without hanging around here and helping you. Nobody asked *me* to babysit this afternoon."

Billy saw the point. He collected and laid out the instruments.

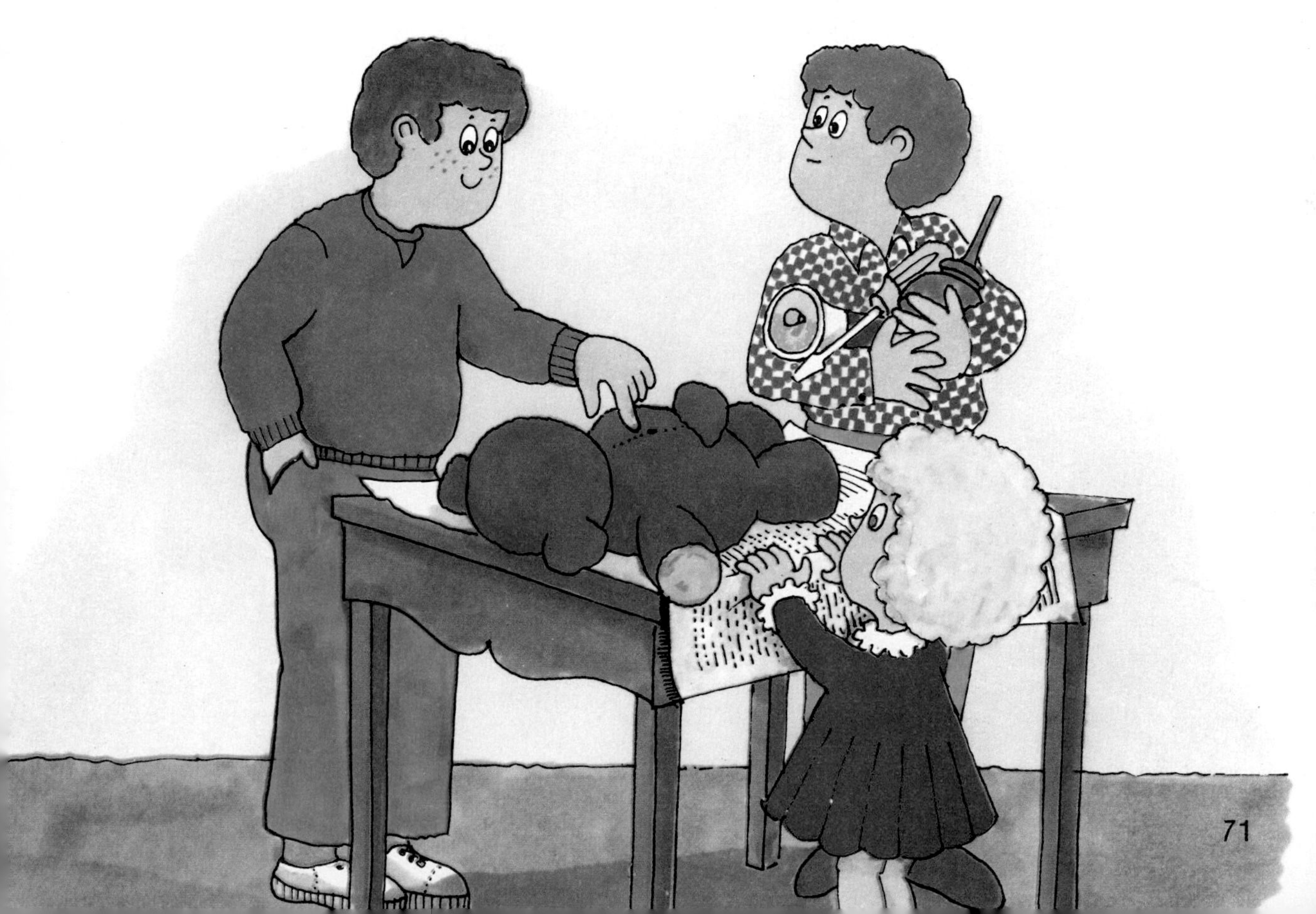

The Wind-up Patient

"Razor blade," said Fats, and Billy handed it to him. Fats slit the stitches and pulled the cloth fur open.

"Screwdriver," ordered Fats, holding out his hand. He prodded cautiously around in the patient.

"Machinery's in a box," he said. "It's bigger

than I thought. Razor blade again." He slit a few more stitches.

"Flashlight," he requested, and squinted into the patient's middle. "The box lid is screwed on tight and I can't get at it," he reported. "I'd better take the whole works out. Screwdriver."

Fats pushed the patient's stuffings away from the box and lifted it right out. Billy crowded up to look as Fats unscrewed the wooden lid and took it off.

"Why, it's a music box," said Billy. "Boy, look at that rust."

"A music box!" exclaimed Fats. "Hot diggity! If only it'll still play — "

"I don't see anything broken," said Billy.

"Hand me the oil can," said Fats, "and go see if you've got an old wind-up key anywhere."

By the time Billy got back with the key out of an old engine, Fats had oiled the music box and was wiping off the rust with the tail of his shirt. He fitted the key into the keyhole and turned carefully.

A few notes tinkled out, too slowly to make a tune.

"The operation was a success," said Billy. "We have saved the patient's life."

"We've saved *my* life, you mean," said Fats. "Oh brother, can I ever use this old music box! I'll bet Ellen won't even notice the difference."

"Ellen?" repeated Billy. "What are you talking about, anyway?"

"That's what I broke today of Ellen's," explained Fats. "She has a fancy box she keeps bracelets and junk in, and it's got a music box in the bottom. At least it *did* have. I wound it up too tight and broke the spring that makes it go. But if I hurry, I can slip this music box in, instead, before she gets home and finds out."

"Say, whose music box do you think this music box is, anyway?" demanded Billy.

"Now listen, be reasonable," pleaded Fats. "I really need this, no fooling, and Gloria won't care. Will you, Gloria?"

But Gloria was staring at her bear. "My bear!" she wailed. Tears streamed down her cheeks. "I want my BEAR!"

"Listen to that," said Billy angrily. "Swipe a poor little kid's music box, would you? Besides, when her mother gets back, I'm the one that would get in trouble. You just go to work and put that thing back."

"All right, all right," grumbled Fats. "Some pal you turned out to be." He squeezed the music box back into the patient so the wind-up key stuck out the back. Then he stuffed the stuffings in and sewed up the seam.

He tossed the bear to Billy. "Don't come to me looking for help with baby-sitting again, that's all," said Fats, and started for the door.

Billy wound up the key as tightly as it would go, and held the bear out to Gloria. Just as she reached for it, the music box buzzed, and then started playing, loud and fast. Gloria snatched her hand away and her mouth dropped open. Then she backed clear across the room and burst into tears.

"Well, how do you like that!" exclaimed Billy. "And after we work our fingers to the bone for her. What's the matter with her, anyway?"

Fats came back into the room. "She's scared of the noise," he explained. "Little kids are funny that way."

"But what'll I *do*?" shouted Billy, as the music played and Gloria shrieked.

"Here. Give it to me." Fats laid the bear out on the operating table again. "Get stuffings," he ordered. "Old rags or anything."

Even before the music ran down, Fats had the music box out on the table again. Billy handed him a torn dishcloth and five old socks, and Fats stuffed them into the space where the music box had been.

"Cookies," ordered Fats, as he started sewing the patient up again.

"*What*?" asked Billy.

"You heard me," said Fats. "Cookies."

Billy went and got a box of cookies.

Fats finished his sewing. Then he sat down beside Gloria with the bear and the box of cookies. By the time Billy got the operating table cleared off and the instruments put away, Fats and Gloria had polished off the cookies. Gloria was smiling and cuddling her bear.

Then Billy's mother and Gloria's mother opened the front door. By the time they got into the room, the music box was gone off the table, and there was a squarish bulge in Fats's pants pocket.

"And what did you do while mummy was gone, darling?" asked Gloria's mother. Gloria wasn't saying a word.

"We mostly played with her bear," said Billy.

"Oh, that old thing, she drags it with her everywhere. You'd never think it now, but it was beautiful when she got it. It was a present. Very expensive, I'm sure. It used to wind up and play music, but it's been broken for ages."

"Billy's very clever with machinery," said Billy's mother proudly. "Why don't you let him see if he can mend it? He'd love to try, I'm sure."

Fats edged toward the door. "I'd better be going now," he mumbled. "There's something I've got to do."

"If Billy can fix it, that would be wonderful!" exclaimed Gloria's mother. "Billy's going to mend your bear, darling. He'll take it all apart, and fix it so it plays music. Give Billy your bear, like a good girl."

That was the last straw for Gloria. She howled, "No, no, no, NO!" Then she kicked Billy on the shin.

"Dear me, I don't know what's gotten into her," apologized her mother. "I expect we'd better go now. It's past her nap time."

After they had gone, Billy's mother said, "What a shame she wouldn't let you fix her bear! It would have been such fun to watch her face when the old bear started playing music again!"

"Would it? I mean, yes, wouldn't it?" said Billy. Then he shouted, "Hey, Fats! Wait up. I'll come along and help you."

AUTHOR

Billy and Fats have appeared in many magazine stories and in two books: *Billy Had a System* and *Billy's Clubhouse.* Probably one reason Marion Holland writes such amusing stories about children is that she has five children of her own. She says she also gets story ideas from memories of her own childhood.

Mrs. Holland first worked as an artist, drawing pictures for other people's stories. She then decided to try to write a story herself. She sold her first story the day after she finished it! She has been writing ever since and also appears on educational TV programs.

Other books of Mrs. Holland's that you might also enjoy are *Casey Jones Rides Vanity, The Secret Horse,* and *No Children, No Pets.*

Beware, My Child

Beware, my child,
of the snaggle-toothed beast.
He sleeps till noon,
then makes his feast
on Hershey bars
and cakes of yeast
and anyone around — o.

So when you see him,
sneeze three times
and say three loud
and senseless rhymes
and give him all your
saved-up dimes,
or else you'll ne'er be found — o.

— SHEL SILVERSTEIN

Before You Spend That Coin...

by Eva Knox Evans

You may begin to put interesting coins into a box somewhere instead of into your pocket. You may begin wondering about them and talking about them and reading about them.

All of us know that money will buy things. But have you ever thought of money as being something that is interesting and beautiful? Once you begin looking at coins that way, you may decide that a certain penny or nickel will be a lot more fun to keep than it will be to spend.

What is more, you will soon discover that sometimes your nickel isn't just five cents at all, but worth twenty cents or even seventy-five. You will look twice before you spend any of your coins, for it would be a shame to pay $1.50 for a chocolate bar because the dime you used was worth that instead of ten cents.

Before you know it, you'll be a coin collector!

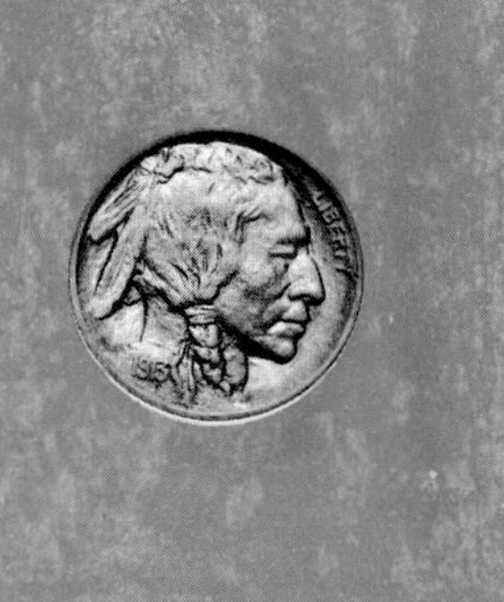

You will probably begin collecting with the money in your pocket. Or your mother may send you to the grocery store, and as soon as you get home you will spread the change on the kitchen table and begin to look it over carefully. Then you may lay aside a new Kennedy half-dollar, a 1932 Lincoln penny, and a Buffalo nickel, and replace them with some more ordinary money of your own.

When you begin collecting, the first thing you will want to know is how much each coin is worth. After all, money is money, and all of it is worth something. But what makes some coins more valuable than others? What can make a certain penny worth not one cent but $6.50 instead?

An old coin can be valuable, or it can be worth nothing at all except as an interesting piece. A new coin can be worth a lot of money or worth only what you can buy with it.

One of the most important things about a coin is whether it looks worn or new. No matter what date is on it, a bright, new, shiny coin is worth putting aside until you can find out other things about it.

Scarce coins are valuable. Each year the Director of the United States Mint decides how many pennies, nickels, dimes, quarters, and half-dollars the mints will make that year. Money wears out and gets lost, and sometimes more of one kind of coin is needed than of another.

For instance, in 1915 the San Francisco mint made only about one and a half million nickels.

In 1916, they made almost twelve million. So those San Francisco 1915 nickels, because they are scarcer, are worth three times as much as the 1916 ones.

Some of the older coins, too, are worth almost a fortune because there are so few of them. There were 17,796 five-dollar gold pieces minted in 1822. Today only three of them are known to be left. One of them is at a museum in Washington. The other two are owned by private collectors. Each of these three gold pieces might possibly bring over $20,000 now. No one knows what happened to the other 17,793. Suppose you found one!

The designs of our coins are changed from time to time. Because of this, even modern coins that are no longer minted can become valuable. You must be sure, of course, that these coins are in pretty good shape before you save them for your collection. Watch for Indian Head pennies, Liberty Head nickels, Buffalo nickels, and Liberty Standing quarters. Lay them aside until you have a chance to see how valuable they are before you spend them.

We have two cities now in the United States where our mints are located. Each mint has a "mint mark": "P" for Philadelphia, and "D" for Denver. San Francisco had a mint until 1955, and so you will still find some coins with the "S" for that mint.

You can be sure that all United States coins without any mint mark were made in Philadelphia. Philadelphia put its mint mark only on the Jefferson nickel it made from 1942 to 1945. The other two mints put their initials on all their coins.

Philadelphia has usually made more coins than the other mints. Coins with a "D" or an "S" are sometimes more valuable because there aren't so many of them.

There are dealers all over the country who buy and sell coins. You can find out from them what different coins are worth.

You will find collecting much more interesting if you begin to specialize at once. One way that is fun is to try to find a Lincoln penny for each year that they

have been minted, or a Jefferson nickel for each year. This won't be as easy as it sounds, for you will find that it grows harder

and harder as you hunt for earlier coins. As you go along, you will want to take out the coins that are worn looking as soon as you find some of the same date in better condition. Of course, the brand-new ones are the very best of all to save.

The study of coins and money is called **numismatics**. There are magazines and books about coin collecting. There are clubs where you can learn about collecting and where you can exchange coins and show off the ones you prize.

Once you become a coin collector, you won't stop being one as you grow older. A coin collection that may not be worth very much now can be a very valuable thing in twenty years or even sooner. Many people who started coin collecting as a hobby when they were young have sold their collections to our great museums. Those pennies that you collect now may be dollars later on.

AUTHOR

The article you have just read is from *The Adventure Book of Money* by Eva Knox Evans.

Eva Knox Evans was born in Roanoke, Virginia, and began writing when she was a child. Her father was a minister and liked to have the house quiet on Sunday afternoons. Since she and her sister and two brothers were not allowed to play noisy games on Sundays, she used the time to write.

Eva Knox Evans was teaching in Atlanta, Georgia, when she wrote *Araminta,* her first success. She says that her school children helped her write it. "And children have been helping me ever since," she says. "I couldn't write without them."

After her marriage to Boris Witte, they lived in Alaska and then New Hampshire. Mrs. Witte has written many books. Under the name of Eva Knox Evans, some of these are *Skookum, All About Us,* and *Sleepy Time. People Are Important* is a winner of the Jane Addams Children's Book Award, and *The Snow Book* won an award from the Boys Clubs of America in 1966.

Under her married name, Eve Witte, she and her daughter Pat are the authors of *Who Lives Here* and *Touch Me Book.* Mrs. Witte now lives in Cambridge, Massachusetts.

Skill Lesson 2:

RECOGNIZING AND UNDERSTANDING METAPHORS

Can you find the simile in the following sentence?

> On the school playground, Paul is usually as noisy as a howling dog.

You can see that Paul is being compared to a howling dog. The simile tells you that Paul is very noisy on the playground. The word *as* coming before and after *noisy* helps you to know that "as noisy as a howling dog" is a simile.

Now read the next sentence:

1. When Paul gets back to the classroom, however, he becomes a quiet little mouse.

That sentence says that Paul turns into a mouse when

he comes back to class. You know that such a thing could not really happen. Boys just don't turn into mice. The writer left out the signal words *as* or *like* and expected you to think them to yourself. He could have used the simile ". . . becomes *as* quiet *as* a little mouse," but he thought the idea would get across more strongly if he wrote what he did. Saying something that just couldn't be true gets the reader's attention.

When a comparison of two different things is made without using the words *as, than,* or *like,* that comparison is called a **metaphor.**

When a writer says that something acts in a way you know is impossible, that may also be a metaphor. For example, think what the word *flew* in this sentence means:

2. Jack flew around the corner with the other boys after him.

Could a boy really fly unless he was in an airplane? No! The word *flew* in that sentence is telling you that Jack went around the corner so fast that his feet didn't seem to touch the ground at all. In that way Jack was like a flying bird. The word *flew* in that sentence is a metaphor.

A writer is also using a metaphor when he describes someone or something with words that you know couldn't really be true of that person or thing. For

example, notice the word *iron* in the following description:

3. He had muscles of iron.

Are men's muscles ever made of iron? No! The writer wants you to know that the man's muscles were strong just as iron is strong.

When a word or group of words says something you know couldn't actually be true, remember that it may be a metaphor. You should make sure you know what the writer is trying to tell you in that metaphor. Usually you will know right away. If you don't, try doing these things:

A. Make sure you know what word or group of words says something that couldn't really be true.
B. Think what two things the writer wants you to compare with each other.
C. Think how those two things might be alike.
D. Decide which of the ways in which they might be alike makes the most sense in what you are reading.

See if you can do those four things now with the metaphors in each of the following sentences:

4. The house had so little furniture in it that it was just a big old barn.
5. From then until the bell rang, Bobby was a busy little beaver.
6. After supper, Father felt sorry he'd been so bad-tempered and said, "I hope you'll forgive me for having been such a bear this afternoon."
7. The moon was peeking shyly over the tops of the hills to the east.
8. Joe glued his eyes to the magician's hands, but he still couldn't figure out where all those colored handkerchiefs were coming from.
9. His velvet voice has made him a real success as a radio singer.

Discussion

Help your class answer these questions:

1. How is a metaphor like a simile? How is it different?
2. How can you tell when you may be reading a metaphor?
3. Why do writers often use metaphors?
4. What three things can you do to help you figure out the meaning of a metaphor?

5. In each of Sentences 4 through 9, what is the metaphor? What two things are being compared in each of those metaphors? How are those two things alike?

On your own

Find the metaphor in each of the following sentences, and figure out what the speaker or writer means by using that metaphor.

1. Mr. Lee's friend said, "Pete, your store has turned out to be a gold mine, hasn't it?"
2. "Stop repeating every single word I say, you parrot!" said Jim to his baby brother.
3. The ball jumped right out of the boy's glove.
4. The walls were so filthy that they cried out for someone to use some soap and water on them.
5. The barn door groaned loudly on its hinges as we pushed it open.
6. The look she gave him was so icy that he knew something he said must have hurt her feelings.

Checking your work

If you are asked to do so, tell what the metaphor is in one of the above sentences. Then help your class decide whether that metaphor was a good way for the writer to get his idea across.

THE PROBLEM

This morning Doctor Heath
(The dentist) drilled my teeth
And filled them with some silver sitting handy,
And looking pretty mad
Because my teeth were bad,
He ordered me to stay away from candy.

Then later I went by
To visit Doctor Bly,
Who gave me shots for polio and flu;
And since he can't recall
That I'm no longer small,
He offered me a lollypop or two.

I wondered what reply
To give to Doctor Bly.
Was I to say that candy ruins teeth?
Or let the matter drop
And *eat* a lollypop
And risk the future wrath of Doctor Heath?

— *Kaye Starbird*

from

PAUL BUNYAN Swings His Axe

by Dell J. McCormick

Many tales are told of Paul Bunyan, the giant woodsman. Mightiest hero of the North Woods! He was a man of great size and strength who was taller than the trees of the forest. They tell of his mighty deeds and strange adventures from Maine to California.

PAUL BUNYAN DIGS THE ST. LAWRENCE RIVER

One summer Paul decided to go to Maine to visit his father and mother. When he arrived, they talked about old times, and Paul asked about Billy Pilgrim, the biggest man in that part of the country.

"What is this Billy Pilgrim doing?" asked Paul.

"He is digging the St. Lawrence River between the United States and Canada," said Paul's father. "There was nothing to separate the two countries. People never knew when they were in the United States and when they were in Canada."

Paul Bunyan went to see Billy. He found that Billy Pilgrim and his men had been digging for three years and had dug only a very small ditch. Paul laughed when he saw it.

"My men could dig the St. Lawrence River in three weeks," said Paul.

This made Billy angry, for he thought no one could dig a large river in three weeks.

"I will give you a million dollars if you can dig the St. Lawrence River in three weeks!" said Billy Pilgrim.

So Paul sent for some of his friends. Babe the Blue Ox, Ole the Big Swede, Brimstone Bill, and all of Paul's woodsmen joined him.

Paul told Ole to make a huge scoop shovel as large as a house. They fastened it to Babe with a long buckskin rope. He hauled many tons of dirt every day and emptied the scoop shovel in Vermont. You can see the large piles of dirt there to this day. They are called the Green Mountains.

Billy Pilgrim was afraid they would finish digging the river on time. He did not want to pay Paul Bunyan the million dollars, for at heart he was a miser. So he thought of a plan to keep Paul from finishing his work.

One night Billy called his men together and said, "When everybody has gone to bed, we'll go out and pour water on the buckskin rope. Buckskin always stretches when it's wet. Babe the Blue Ox will not be able to pull a single shovelful of dirt!"

The next day, Babe started toward Vermont

with the first load of dirt. When he arrived there, he looked around. The huge scoop shovel was nowhere to be seen! For miles and miles the buckskin rope had stretched through the forests and over the hills.

Babe didn't know what to do. He sat down and tried to think. But everyone knows an ox isn't very bright, so he just sat there. After a while, the sun came out and dried the buckskin. It started to shrink to normal size.

Babe planted his large hoofs between two mountains and waited. The buckskin rope kept

shrinking and shrinking. Soon the scoop shovel came into view over the hills. Then Babe emptied it and started back after another load.

In exactly three weeks the St. Lawrence River was all finished. But still Billy Pilgrim did not want to pay Paul the money.

"Very well," said Paul. "I will remove the water!" So he led Babe the Blue Ox down to the River, and Babe drank the St. Lawrence River dry.

Billy Pilgrim only chuckled to himself. He knew that the first rain would fill it again. Soon it began to rain, and the river became as large as ever.

Paul picked up a large shovel.

"If you do not pay the money you owe me, I will fill the river up again," said Paul.

He threw in a shovelful of dirt. He threw in another and another, but still Billy Pilgrim would not pay him the money.

"I will pay you half your money," said Billy.

Paul again picked up his shovel and tossed more dirt into the river.

"I will pay you two thirds of your money," said Billy.

Paul kept throwing more dirt into the river until he had thrown a thousand shovelfuls.

"Stop! I will pay you all your money!" cried Billy.

So Paul Bunyan was finally paid in full for digging the St. Lawrence River. The thousand shovelfuls of dirt are still there.

They are called the Thousand Islands.

THE POPCORN BLIZZARD

After Paul Bunyan had finished digging the St. Lawrence River, he decided to go west. It was summertime, and the forest was sweet with the smell of green trees. The spreading branches cast their cool shadows on the ground.

"We must cross vast plains," said Paul to his men, "where it is so hot that not even a blade of grass can grow. You must not become too thirsty, as there will be very little water to drink."

With Paul and Babe the Blue Ox leading the way, the rest of the camp then started across the plains on their long journey west. In a few days they had left the woods. Now they were knee-deep in sand that stretched out before them for miles and miles. The sun became hotter and hotter!

There was not a tree in sight. Paul Bunyan's men had never before been away from the forest. They missed the cool shade of the trees. Whenever Paul stopped to rest, thirty or forty men would stand in his shadow to escape the boiling sun.

"I won't be able to last another day," cried Brimstone Bill, "if it doesn't begin to cool off soon!"

It became so hot that the men were exhausted and refused to go another step. Hot Biscuit Slim, the cook, had complained that there was very little food left in the camp. That night Paul took Babe the Blue Ox and went on alone into the mountains to the north. In the mountains Paul found a farmer with a barnful of corn.

"I will buy your corn," said Paul to the farmer. He loaded all the corn on Babe's back and started for camp.

By the time he arrived there, the sun was shining again, and the day grew hotter as the sun arose overhead. Soon it became so hot that the corn started popping. It shot up into the air in vast clouds of white puffy popcorn.

It kept popping and popping, and soon the air was filled with wonderful white popcorn. It came down all over the camp and almost covered the kitchen. The ground became white with popcorn as far as the eye could see. It fell like a snowstorm until everything was covered two feet deep with fluffy popcorn.

"A snowstorm! A snowstorm!" cried the men as they saw it falling. Never had they seen anything like it before. Some ran into the tents and put on their woolen mittens. Others put on heavy overcoats and woolen caps. They clapped each other on the back and laughed and shouted for joy.

"Let's make snowshoes!" cried Ole the Big Swede. So they all made snowshoes and waded around in the white popcorn and threw popcorn snowballs at each other, and everybody forgot how hot it had been the day before. Even the horses thought it was real snow, and some of them almost froze to death before the men could put woolen blankets on them and lead them to shelter.

Babe the Blue Ox winked at Paul. He knew it was only popcorn.

Paul Bunyan chuckled to himself at the popcorn blizzard and decided to start west again while the men were feeling so happy. He found them all huddled around the kitchen fire.

"Now is the time to move on west," said Paul, "before it begins to get hot again." So they packed up and started. The men waded through the popcorn and blew on their hands to keep them warm. Some claimed that their feet were frostbitten, and others rubbed their ears to keep them from freezing.

After traveling for a few weeks more, they saw ahead of them the great forest they had set out to reach. They cheered Paul Bunyan for leading them safely over the hot desert plains. Babe the Blue Ox laughed and winked at Paul whenever anyone mentioned the great blizzard.

Paul Bunyan is probably the best-known hero in American folklore. The tall tales about him are not true, of course. But very often, such legends grow out of true stories about real people, with the tales growing taller and taller the more they are told. There really was a man named Paul Bunyon, a very strong French-Canadian who was the boss of a

logging camp. People began to tell about things that this man did. Each would try to outdo the other by telling a better story. Many people believe that in this way Paul Bunyon became "Paul Bunyan," the legend. This is also thought to be true of Johnny Appleseed, John Henry, and other folk heroes.

AUTHOR

Dell J. McCormick was born in 1893 and spent much of his early life in northwestern United States. He worked at several different jobs to put himself through college. One such job was in a lumber camp in northern Idaho. It was there that he heard and read many tales of Paul Bunyan. He became interested in these legends and decided to learn more about them.

After finishing college, Mr. McCormick worked in Seattle, Washington, and wrote short stories in his free time. He said that he liked the idea of being a business-man in the daytime and a part-time writer at night. Many books about Paul Bunyan had already been written, but Mr. McCormick decided to write one especially for children. The two tales you have just read are from his book, *Paul Bunyan Swings His Axe.* He also wrote *Tall Timber Tales.*

In his later life, Mr. McCormick moved to Europe, and he died in France in 1949.

MORE BOOKS TO ENJOY

THE BAT-POET, *by Randall Jarrell.*

A little bat makes friends with other animals by making up poems about them.

BURT DOW, DEEP-WATER MAN, *by Robert McCloskey.*

This is a tall tale of a New England fisherman who catches a whale by the tail.

THE CLAMBAKE MUTINY, *by Jerome Beatty, Jr.*

In this amusing story, some trapped lobsters, about to be eaten at a clambake, make their escape.

MR. PETERSAND'S CATS, *by Louis Slobodkin.*

People on a summer island learn an important lesson about kindness to animals.

MY DOG RINTY, *by Ellen Tarry and Marie Hall Ets.*

A boy in a city apartment discovers how to turn his troublesome dog into a very valuable one.

OH, WHAT NONSENSE!, *edited by William Cole.*

This is a collection of poems to read just for fun.

WHO'S IN CHARGE OF LINCOLN?, *by Dale Fife.*

Lincoln Farnum can't seem to help getting into mischief. But the day he ends up on a train headed for Washington is the most amazing of all!

Masquerades

MASQUERADES

A MINOR BIRD *by Robert Frost* 111
MYSTERY GUEST AT LEFT END *by Beman Lord* 112
THE UMPIRE *by Milton Bracker* 137
AT THE BASEBALL GAME SAT MRS. PACE *by Harriet Mandelbaum* 137
A HOUSE FOR AQUANAUTS 138
A CRUST OF BREAD *by Andre Drucker* 140
BEAUTY *by E-Yeh-Shure'* 158
JAZZ 160
Skill Lesson 3: RECOGNIZING PARAGRAPH TOPICS 167
SUMMER *by Kaye Starbird* 172
AS TO THE RESTLESS BROOK *by John Kendrick Bangs* 172
LIMERICKS *by Harriet Mandelbaum and Barbara Clemons* 173
HIS MAJESTY, THE PEASANT *by Sally Werner* 174
THERE WAS A NAUGHTY BOY *by John Keats* 185
A RIDE ON HIGH *by Candida Palmer* 186
E IS THE ESCALATOR *by Phyllis McGinley* 198
TWO MAGIC NUMBERS 199
MARCO COMES LATE *by Dr. Seuss* 200
TWO WEEKS OLD AND ON HIS OWN *by Vitali Bianki* 206
Skill Lesson 4: GETTING HELP FROM COMMAS 216
THE LEAF PILE *by Kaye Starbird* 223
THE HERONS ON BO ISLAND *by Elizabeth Shane* 224
A Story Treasure from WINNIE-THE-POOH *by A. A. Milne* 226
BIBLIOGRAPHY 236

A MINOR BIRD

I have wished a bird would fly away,
And not sing by my house all day;

Have clapped my hands at him from the door
When it seemed as if I could bear no more.

The fault must partly have been in me.
The bird was not to blame for his key.

And of course there must be something wrong
In wanting to silence any song.

– *Robert Frost*

Mystery Guest at Left End

by Beman Lord

The Packers had just lost their sixth football game in a row. They'd have had at least a tie if only Louie Williams, who played left end, could ever hold onto a ball once it was in his hands. As usual, he'd dropped the beautiful pass that Si had thrown him on the last play.

Walking home with his friend John Bradley, Si said, "What we need is a good left end, one who can catch a pass and hold onto it."

"I wish I could run faster," said John. "Maybe if I lost some of this weight . . ."

"Better not try!" Si said. "We need you, and especially that weight, on the line. We've just got to find another left end. Maybe one of us can come up with an idea in the next day or so. Be thinking about it!"

After lunch, Si decided to practice his throwing. He got his football and went out to the backyard. Two tires had been hung from trees. Si stood by one tire, took aim at the other, and threw the ball. It went nicely through the hoop. He then went over and picked up the ball, and

threw it back at the other tire. It sailed right through the hoop again.

"My aim is good," he said aloud. "All I need is someone to catch it."

"That shouldn't be too hard to do with those weak throws," said a voice.

Si looked around, trying to see who had spoken. He couldn't see anyone.

"It's harder than you think, whoever you are, and my throws are not weak."

There was no answer. He picked up the football, looked around again, even up at the trees, and threw the ball at the tire. It missed.

"Not only are the throws weak, but that one was crooked," the voice said calmly.

Si turned quickly, but he still couldn't see anybody. "I don't know who or where you are, but I'm getting sick and tired of your remarks. Either come out and show your face or keep your thoughts to yourself!"

"I'm only trying to be helpful," the voice answered. "And as far as I can see, you need more than a little help."

"It's hard to throw at an old tire," Si shouted back. Then he decided to change his tactics. "You're right. I do need help. How about catching a few passes?"

"Oh, all right. Now that you've asked nicely."

Si saw a girl get up from a lawn chair in the next yard. "I thought it sounded like a girl! But what's the idea of hiding behind a lawn chair?"

The girl crossed over to Si's yard. "My name is Faith Cummings, in case you've forgotten. Your mother introduced us last week. And I wasn't hiding. I've been reading, and I must say your talking has been very annoying."

"So sorry," Si said. "Now if you'll just get back to your own yard, I'll get on with my passing."

"Are you afraid I might be too good?" asked Faith. "As far as I can see, there shouldn't be any problem catching a football. A girl should be able to do it as well as a boy. I've also watched football on TV with my father, so I do have some idea of the game."

"Okay! Okay, Miss Know-it-all, we'll give you a try," Si said, as he picked up the football. "Start running, and I'll throw the ball ahead of you."

Faith started running and was almost across her own backyard before Si threw. It was an excellent pass, and Faith caught it easily.

"Beginner's luck!" Si called. "Stay out there and I'll throw you another."

She caught a short one and a long one and a high one. Si was amazed, then more amazed, and finally flabbergasted.

"Good grief! Who'd have believed it!" he said, under his breath. He then threw her three more passes. She caught them all.

"Do you mind if I rest for a minute? All this running is making me hot." She didn't wait for an answer, but quickly sat down.

Si walked over and pulled up another chair beside her. "I'd better apologize," he said. "Where did you ever learn to catch a football?"

"Nowhere. I can catch a softball quite well, and I didn't think a football would be too difficult.

I've always wanted to try. Thank you. Now, if you don't mind, I think I'll go back to my reading. Would you try to be a little quieter?"

"Will I try to be *what*? Are you crazy? Just because you can catch a football like nobody else, you want me to . . ." Si didn't finish the sentence. Suddenly his temper lessened. What an idea! Would it work? He'd have to talk it over with John. He started toward the house. Halfway there he turned and called politely, "You know, you were good."

"Yes, I know it. Thank you," she answered, without looking up from her book.

Si made a face and went into the house.

The Secret Deal

When John answered the telephone, Si said, "Drop whatever you're doing and get over here quickly. I think I've found a left end."

"Who?" John asked. "Where'd he come from? Has he just moved into town?"

"Came in last week. No more questions. Just get over here on the double. She might leave. I mean, it might leave. It's temperamental." Si was getting confused. "Just get over here." He hung up.

Si went out to the front porch. Within five minutes, John arrived.

"Where is he?" he asked, as he came up onto the porch. "I want to see him catch."

"Sit down, John," Si said very seriously. "I think I'd better tell you how it all started. Don't interrupt until I finish."

But when Si came to the part where Faith had come over to his yard, John burst out, "You mean to tell me that Faith Cummings is our new left end? You got me away from the Ohio State-Purdue game to tell me this? A girl! I lost five pounds just running over here."

"Hold your horses until I finish the story. It's

unbelievable," Si said. He quickly told John the rest. "I threw seven passes, and she didn't miss once. Imagine what we would do with her on the team!"

"I don't believe it. I've got to see it done. Let's go," John said, as he got up from his chair.

"Hold it," Si said. "I have a plan. She's pretty touchy. I'll flatter her into catching a few more, and then you come around the house quietly and watch. She might not do it if we both went back there together."

Faith was still reading. She looked up as Si came up to her chair, but she didn't say anything.

"I hate to interrupt you, but you were terrific! I still can't believe what I saw. Would you mind catching a few more passes?" Si asked politely.

Faith sighed. "Oh, all right," she said. "Do you think three or four would be enough? I would like to finish this book sometime today."

"Thanks. Stay right here and I'll get the ball." As he raced over to his yard, he noticed John

coming quietly up between the two houses. He gave him a nod and picked up the ball.

"Cut across your lawn slowly," Si yelled. "The ball will be waiting for you."

Faith did so and without any trouble caught the ball. Si threw her another. She caught it. The next two she also caught.

"I think that should prove to you that it wasn't beginner's luck," she said, as she walked back to her chair. "After all, I haven't missed one yet."

Si dashed around the house and motioned for John to follow him to the front porch. "Well," Si said, "do you believe it now? She hasn't missed once. Can you imagine how many games we could have won with her on our side?"

John shook his head. "I can't believe it. How does she do it?"

"The question isn't *how* does she do it — she *does* it, period. The question is will she do it for the team?" Si said. "I've been thinking. If we dressed her up in my brother's old uniform, no one would ever know she was a girl."

"It's touch football, so she won't be tackled," John said, warming up to the idea. "It certainly is worth a try. We've got to do something if the Packers are ever going to win a game. You ask her, and I'll back you up. Try flattering her again."

John and Si approached the lawn chair nervously. Si spoke first. "This is my friend, John Bradley. We're sorry to bother you, but could you give us five minutes of your time?"

She nodded to John. "Nice to meet you. Please sit down." She looked at her watch. "Three minutes is all I can spare. I still have the lunch dishes to do, and my mother will be fussing about them."

The boys pulled up chairs, and Si explained the problem. He ended by saying, "We need a good left end. You'd be sensational. We thought, and hoped, that you might help us out for our last two games." Si paused and waited for a reply. Faith just looked at both of them.

"You could wear Si's brother's uniform, and no one would know you're a girl," John said.

Faith glared at John. "I'm rather proud to be a girl."

"Well, look at it this way," Si said. "You could be our mystery guest."

She sat up. "How much do you pay?"

"Pay!" Si yelled. "This is for sport. We don't get paid anything. We do it for the fun."

"I agree boys do it for the fun, but for girls it's a different matter. I imagine there will be some work involved — practice and all that — and mystery guests do get paid."

John and Si looked at each other. "We don't have much money," John said weakly.

"It doesn't have to be money," Faith answered. "Just let me think for a minute."

While she was thinking, her mother came to the back door and called, "Faith, you haven't forgotten the dishes?"

"No, Mother. I'll be right there." Her mother closed the door, and Faith said to the boys, "If there's one thing I hate to do, it's dishes. Perhaps you'd like to help?"

"How much?" Si asked.

Faith smiled. "All right, I'll be your left end, and you two will be my dishwashers."

"What are you going to tell your folks?" John asked.

"I'll tell them we have a secret deal," Faith said.

"That's just the point," Si exclaimed. "If we decide to do it, you'll have to promise to keep it a secret."

Faith shrugged. "I promise. Now, if you'd like to talk it over before you decide, today's dishes can wait another minute."

The boys walked over to Si's yard, talked for a few minutes, and returned. "I'll wash," said Si, "and John will dry. Lead the way."

"George" Joins the Team

Friday night Si brought over the uniform.

"I'll try it on in the cellar," said Faith. A few minutes later she reappeared. "It fits fine."

"Good," Si said. "John and I will be by tomorrow about 8:30, and we'll all go down to the field together. Be ready then, okay?"

"It's rather early, but I'll be ready. After all, you've kept your share of the bargain, and I'll keep mine."

The next morning Faith appeared dressed in the football uniform and helmet, carrying a pocketbook and wearing pink slippers.

"Good grief! Are you nutty?" John cried, pointing to her shoes and pocketbook.

"I thought you might enjoy a little joke, but I can see you don't. You do take this game seriously." She disappeared and then came back wearing sneakers.

"Now let me do all the talking when we get there," Si said, as they started for the field. "Just remember you're my cousin visiting for the weekend and your name is George Matthews. You won't start the game, but you'll play when we need you. You're shy, and you don't like to talk. Just be sure you keep your promise about not telling you're a girl. And keep your ponytail under your helmet!"

When they reached the field, Si introduced the new player to the team. The game started with Faith, or George, on the bench. She didn't play the first quarter at all, but she played off and on the rest of the game. She caught five out of five passes, made two touchdowns, and gained many, many yards. The Packers won their first game. The team crowded around Faith and kept patting her on the back. Si and John tried to get her away before anyone could realize she was a girl. They were also not sure

how much pounding she could take before losing her temper. They finally got her away and started for home.

"This calls for a celebration," Si said, as they left the field. "We'll all stop at Pete's Drugstore, and I'll do the treating. You were just great, George!"

"Thank you, but you now can call me Faith. I was rather good, don't you think, John?"

"You were a pro," John said. "You fooled everybody. Those Steelers never knew *what* a mystery guest we had!"

They reached the drugstore and found a table in the back. Faith started to remove her helmet.

"Do you want to give the whole thing away?" Si exclaimed. "I know it'll be uncomfortable eating ice cream, but could you leave it on for another ten minutes?"

Faith said, "All right. I'll have a hot fudge sundae with strawberry ice cream."

"That's forty cents!" Si said. "I wasn't planning to celebrate quite *that* much. But it isn't every day that the Packers win a game." They gave their order, and after a few minutes the waitress brought it.

"I just love these sundaes and never seem to get enough of them. I could eat one every day of the week," said Faith.

"Boy, wait until next week and we win another one," John said to Si. "We should have had her playing for us the whole season."

Faith put down her spoon. "I didn't want to talk business while we were eating. But now that you've brought up the matter of next week's game, there's one small question. How much?"

"The usual fee," Si said. "Dishes for a week."

"My mother says you are not getting them clean enough. However, I do happen to have

another idea. These sundaes are delicious. Starting tomorrow, I'd like a standing order of one every day next week."

"Why, that's . . ." John said, counting on his fingers. "That's $2.80!"

"Very good," Faith answered. "$1.40 apiece. You said yourself I was a pro."

John and Si looked at each other. "Okay," Si said halfheartedly. "You can have a sundae every day."

"Thank you," said Faith. "And now I must run. I'll see you on Tuesday and Thursday for practice."

Both boys nodded.

Decoy

As Si and John were walking to Faith's house on Tuesday, Si said, "I've been worrying about Faith and next Saturday's game. Do you realize they'll be out to get her on every play?"

John stopped dead in his tracks. "We need her to catch your passes! But on the other hand, we wouldn't want her to get hurt."

After talking some more, they decided to tell Faith that she shouldn't play. While they waited for her to come out of her house, Si said, "Don't feel too bad, John. We did win one game this season."

When Faith appeared, Si said, "John and I have been talking about Saturday's game. It's going to be rougher, and they'll try to block you on every play, after last week's game. We both think it might be better if you didn't play, and we're releasing you from our bargain."

Faith started to laugh and then realized how serious the boys were. "I'm sorry, but you know I'm not all that tender. And I took quite a few blocks in the last game. Thanks for the offer, but I'm going to play."

"Do you realize you're going to be a sitting duck?" John exclaimed.

"Yes," Faith said, "a sitting duck and probably a decoy, too."

"You both have said the magic words!" cried Si. "I think everything's going to be all right. We are going to have a mystery guest decoy."

George, or Faith, turned out to be exactly that in the game. Si used her for only two plays in the first quarter. The Steelers naturally expected a pass and guarded her. Si faked passing both times and ran with the ball. The first play netted twenty yards, and the second play brought the Packers a touchdown. He didn't use her in the second or third quarters, but then in the last quarter the Steelers tied it up. Si called George in and called time out.

"We're confusing them," Si said to the team. "George will go out for a pass. Most of their backfield will be guarding him and the rest rushing me. I'll throw to Ernie and he'll run around the right end. Let's go!"

The play worked exactly as Si said it would, and they gained fifteen yards.

"Good, we're getting there." Si patted Ernie on the back. "We're really confusing them. This time, I'll throw to George."

The team broke from the huddle and took their

places on the line. George, or Faith, was playing a wide left end. She had figured that this gave her freedom to get around her blocker and either run left or right of him. She heard the signal, sidestepped her blocker, and raced down the field. She ran straight for about ten yards and then cut across the field.

Si spotted her and threw the ball. When she saw that it was going over her head, she ran back and made a jump for the ball. She couldn't get hold of it, and it bounced off her fingers into the hands of Bob Taylor, the Packers' right end. Bob had tried to pull the Steelers away from

"George" by pretending the pass was coming to him, but it hadn't worked. He had then raced across the field to give "George" blocking. He never broke his stride as the ball landed in his hands, and he raced for a touchdown.

As she came down from her jump, Faith was off balance, and she stumbled into the Steelers' halfback. The force threw her to the ground, and her helmet came tumbling off. She sprang to her feet.

"Of all the nerve! Why don't you watch where you're going?" she said to the amazed Steeler.

"I was standing still!" Then he realized what he was seeing. "Fellows," he yelled. "George is a girl! He's that new girl!"

Both teams gathered around. John and Si stood back, waiting to hear the razzing. It didn't come. Instead they heard:

"A girl? Who would have thought it?"

"Where did you learn to catch like that?"

"Will you play for us next year?"

Faith listened for a while and then said, "Thank you for all the compliments. But I believe I've had enough football for this or any year. Now, if you'll excuse me, you can get back to your game." She picked up her helmet, smiled at John and Si, and walked off the field.

All the boys watched her go and gave her a round of applause. She turned and waved.

No one scored in the last minutes of the game. The Packers won 13–6.

After the game, John said to Si, "The celebration is on me today." As they walked into Pete's, there sat Faith, all alone, eating her last hot fudge sundae.

She signaled to them, and the boys went over and joined her. "I'm almost finished, but I wanted to say thank you for the sundaes."

"We want to thank you for keeping your part of the bargain. You played a terrific game," John said.

She finished the last of her ice cream and stood up. "Thank you. I did, didn't I? Girls can be useful sometimes, don't you think? Now I'm going to get out of this uniform and into some decent clothes."

The boys didn't say anything. John ordered and they just sat there. The waitress brought their order and left. Each picked up a straw and started to drink from the one bottle of soda pop.

Finally Si said, "You don't suppose she plays basketball, do you?"

AUTHOR

Beman Lord wrote *Mystery Guest at Left End* for his nieces, who complained that there weren't enough girls in his stories! There is also a girl in *Shot Put Challenge.* But all of Beman Lord's sports books are popular with both boys and girls. Two of them — *Quarterback's Aim* and *The Trouble with Francis* — have won awards from the Boys Clubs of America. Some of his other books are *Bats and Balls, Guards for Matt,* and a science-fiction book called *The Day the Spaceship Landed.*

Beman Lord, his wife, and their two children live in New York City. Mr. Lord says of his own writing, "What I am trying to say in all my stories is that sports can be fun, and you don't have to be a great athlete to play them. I wasn't. I am thin and wear glasses. Yet I played all sports and had a good time."

At the baseball game sat Mrs. Pace,
When the crowd cheered, "He stole a base!"
  She said, "Oh, my land!
  This game should be banned,
To cheer 'stealing' is a public disgrace!"

—Harriet Mandelbaum

THE UMPIRE

The umpire is a lonely man
Whose calls are known to every fan
Yet none will call him Dick or Dan
  In all the season's games.
They'll never call him Al or Ed
Or Bill or Phil or Frank or Fred
Or Jim or Tim or Tom or Ted—
  They'll simply call him names.

—Milton Bracker

A HOUSE FOR AQUANAUTS

How would you like to live on the ocean floor? Four scientists lived in this four-room underwater home at the bottom of the ocean for two months.

You have read and seen a great deal both in newspapers and on TV about the astronauts who explore space. Men who explore under the surface of the sea are called aquanauts.

The large picture shown here is a cut-away drawing that shows what the underwater home of the aquanauts looked like inside as well as outside. In many ways the rooms looked like those in an ordinary house or apartment. The underwater home even had a TV set and a refrigerator. There was also another kind of

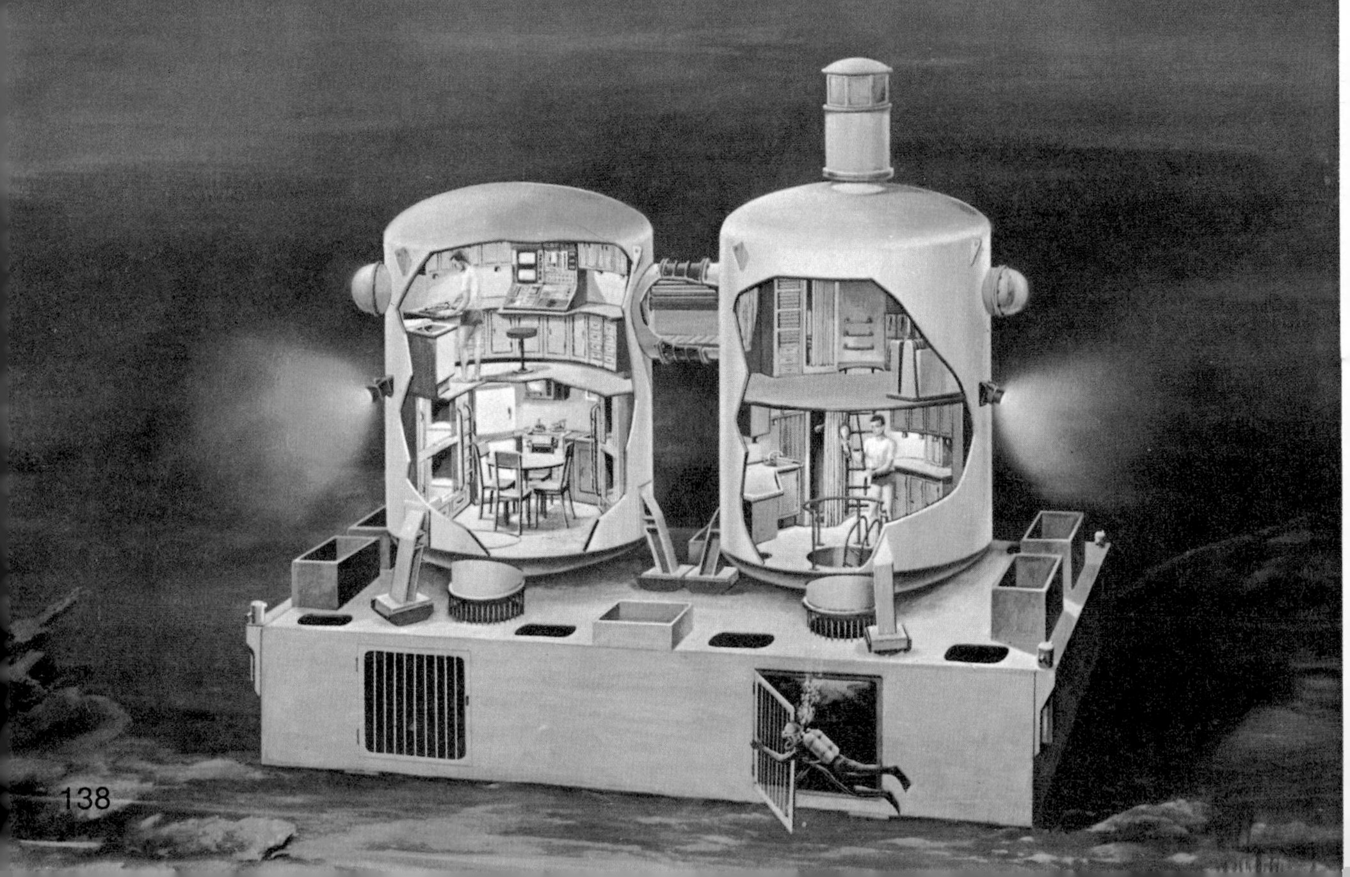

TV set — a set like the one used in space exploration. This TV sent pictures back to scientists on land so that they could see the aquanauts as they lived in the house and explored the sea around it.

The photograph at the left on this page shows the aquanauts at work exploring the ocean. The picture on the right shows the capsule used to bring the aquanauts back to the surface.

As explorers travel more into outer space, they realize that there is much that is still not known about the planet Earth, especially the oceans. We will surely learn much more about the oceans in the near future from the aquanaut scientists.

A long time ago, there was a peasant who had a son named Jan. He was a poor peasant, with only a small plot of land. He worked very hard, but he remained poor. Sometimes he went to bed hungry.

Jan was growing quickly. He was always hungry. He could eat anything, but he liked meat best of all. Except for Sundays, there was never any meat on the table. Meat was too expensive. Jan grew tired of eating potatoes and bread all the week long. If only he could eat meat every day!

One morning, when there was only bread and gravy for breakfast, he said to his father, "Will there be no meat again today?"

"No," said his father. "Meat is too expensive."

"Then I will go away," said Jan. "I have had enough bread. I am tired of it. Bread, bread, bread, and never any meat! I am going away. I am leaving home."

"Where do you want to go?" asked his father.

"I shall go into the world. The world is a big place. I am sure that there are better places than this village. I will try my luck in the big world."

"Do you think that the big world is waiting for you with pots of meat?" asked his father. "Stay at home. Help me with the work. Things will get better one day."

But Jan had made up his mind. He had had enough of home and bread, bread, bread every day. He went to his room. He stuffed some of his belongings into a knapsack, and off he went into the big world.

Jan whistled a tune as he marched along. After a few hours' walk, he began to feel hungry.

At noon he came to a village. He could see by the flags and colored wagons that there was a fair. Musicians in the market square played for the people to dance.

Jan joined them. He danced as briskly as anyone. But it made him feel hungrier than ever. He had no money to buy food. Where could he get something to eat?

He walked out of the village. There, just off the road, was a large white house. Leaning out of one of the windows was a man, listening to the music. Although Jan did not know it, this man was the squire of the village.

"This is a rich house," thought Jan. "There should be plenty of meat here."

Jan took his cap from his head and said, "Excuse me, sir! Can you spare me something from your table?"

The squire looked at him for a long time. He turned and took something from the table.

"Take this!" he said.

He dropped it into Jan's cap. It was a crust of bread.

Jan had expected meat. But what did he get? Bread! He was so angry that he took the crust of bread and threw it into the road as though it were a stone.

"Why did you do that?" called the squire.

"Bread!" Jan grunted. "I am tired of it. I have it at home, day in and day out. I came into the big world to get something else. You could at least have given me a slice of meat."

The squire gave him another good look and said, "Is that what you want? Why, come in and help yourself. You can have as much as you like. You are welcome."

Jan could scarcely believe his ears. He could have as much meat as he wanted!

Jan lost no time sitting down at the table in the big dining room of the great house. The squire called to his housekeeper, "Mary! Bring the big joint of meat out of the oven! I have a guest!"

The housekeeper brought a joint, steaming in lovely gravy. Jan got ready to help himself.

"Wait a minute," said the squire, smiling. "Before you eat, there is one thing I must tell you. You can eat as much of the joint as you like. But there is a condition."

Jan was impatient to get at the meat.

"What is the condition, sir?" he asked.

"It is quite simple. Because you threw away the bread, I want to teach you to value it better. So, before you eat this meat, you must promise me something. Promise me that you will stay with me until we bake the new bread. Tomorrow we are going to sow the wheat. Until this wheat becomes bread, you can have as much meat as you like. But you will not be allowed to eat any bread, not a crust, not a crumb. Do you understand?"

"Yes, sir."

"If you do not like this condition, you had better go."

"Go? Do you call that a condition? Of course I will promise! I can do very well without bread, forever if need be. Give me meat every time."

"Think it over, my lad," said the squire. "I won't let you go until the harvest is over. If you try to run away, I will tie you to this place with ropes if necessary."

"You won't find me running away from meat!"

"It is a deal, then. Eat to your heart's delight, my lad," said the squire.

Jan ate every bit of the meat down to the bone of the joint. Ah, how wonderful it tasted!

"Well, sir," he said, between two big bites. "What work will I have to do for my food?"

"Not any," said the squire. "Unless you become bored and wish to help a little."

All the meat he wanted and no work! Jan decided that he could not have found a better place in which to stay.

He took the bone from the dish and nibbled at the last bits of meat. The squire only watched him.

Plenty of Meat, But . . .

The next morning Jan was awakened very early by the squire.

"Would you like to join us in the fields?" he said. "We are going to sow the seeds for the bread you will eat after the harvest."

"What bread?" asked Jan sleepily. Then he remembered.

"Certainly, sir. If you do not mind, I will sow it myself."

The farmhands sat around the big table in the huge kitchen. They were served with milk and bread for breakfast, except for Jan, who was given a large slice of steak. All the farmhands eyed his breakfast with envy.

Jan ate it quickly, but to himself he said, "This is greasy stuff so early in the morning. A crust of bread would go well with it. But never mind, meat is always better than bread. Bread is so ordinary."

They went to the fields. Jan walked slowly across the well-plowed field, scattering the wheat as he went.

At noon they sat under a tree to eat their lunch. Jan had as much meat as he wanted. But he was given neither bread nor potatoes.

In the evening it was the same. He had plenty of meat, but nothing else to go with it.

So it was every day. Bread was kept away from Jan as though it were gold or diamonds.

Two weeks passed. Jan ate all the meat he could. He worked when he felt like it. He slept whenever he wished. It was good to live in the big world, where everything was plentiful.

But as the days went by, Jan became restless. He did not feel as well as he did usually. He lost his appetite. On some days he could eat nothing at all. He would sit at the table, stare at his plate, and nibble at the meat.

"What is wrong?" asked the squire one day. "Why don't you eat?"

"I don't feel like it, sir," said Jan. He looked at the farmhands, who were eating bread, lovely home-made bread. "I don't know what is the matter with me. The meat has an unpleasant taste. I would rather have a crust of bread."

"You would, eh?" smiled the squire. "You would not throw it away like a stone?"

He took a crust of bread from the table and threw it to the dog at his feet. "Here, Beppo. Here is something for you!"

The dog looked at the bread. He sniffed it. He turned it over with his nose and pushed it away.

"Oh, you wicked dog!" cried Jan in anger.

He went down on the floor and snatched the bread from the dog. He thrust it into his own mouth.

The squire caught him by the hand and took the bread away. "No, no, my lad. No bread for you until after the harvest."

"Can't I have this crust that the dog has refused?"

"No. You should have had more sense than a dog when you gave me your promise. Eat meat, nothing but meat!"

The servants laughed. Jan blushed with shame. The dog yawned. The squire only smiled.

A Beggar Woman's Kindness

As the days went by, Jan grew worse. He became white and thin. He had lost all taste for meat. He ate it only because he had nothing else. He thought of nothing but bread.

One day he stopped the squire in the farmyard. Jan fell upon his knees.

"Master! Please let me go!" he begged. "Let me go away from here. I cannot stand it any longer. Please release me from my promise!"

"I am sorry, my lad," said the squire. "A promise is a promise. We must keep our agreement. We agreed that you must stay with me until the new bread is ready. I won't let you go. A promise is a promise."

Jan was very unhappy. How could he go on like this? But he could and he did. Though the days and weeks seemed endless, they passed just the same.

Christmas came. The children sang carols, and every house had its Christmas tree. In the big kitchen of the squire's house, Mary was baking some wonderful Christmas breads. Their delicious smell filled the whole house.

Jan was not there to enjoy it. He hid in the stables so that he would not see the delicious loaves which were not for him. Their sight and smell only added to his unhappiness.

The squire went to look for him in the stable.

"Well, Jan, my lad! I am afraid you will have to go hungry today. We have only bread in the house for Christmas Eve."

Jan said sadly, "What a Christmas Eve for me! Today everybody, even the poorest beggar, is feasting. I alone go hungry."

"I am sorry," said the squire. "But there is nothing in my house for you to eat."

"Then at least let me go out and beg for something."

"You can do that if you wish," said the squire.

So Jan went into the streets to beg for something to eat. But into the street behind him went the squire's servants, to make sure that Jan did not run away.

A girl opened the first door on which he knocked.

"A poor traveler wishes you a merry Christmas," he said humbly. "Can you spare me something to eat?"

A woman called from the kitchen, "Give the poor boy a bun. Who is he?"

"It is Jan of the squire's house," said the girl.

"What? He threw bread away! He does not deserve a bun."

The girl shouted so that the whole village could hear: "That serves you right! If bread is too plain for you, you don't need a bun. Go!" She slammed the door.

That happened to him at every house in the village. Nobody would give food to the boy who had wasted bread.

What was Jan to do? He sat down in the snow and cried.

"Why are you crying?" asked a voice.

Jan looked up. In front of him stood an old beggar woman. She was in rags. Her head was bent low. A bag hung heavy on her crooked back. She looked at Jan with great pity.

"Come, come, what is wrong, laddie?"

Jan whimpered. "I am the most unhappy person in all the world."

"Don't talk nonsense," said the beggar woman. "You are young. You are healthy. You can work.

How can you be unhappy? Look at me, an old beggar woman! The cupboards in my house are bare. I am too old for work. I can only beg."

"At least people don't turn you from their doors," said Jan. "But nobody will give me even a crust of bread."

"I can't believe that. This is a kind village. People always give to me."

"But not to me," said Jan, and he told her the whole story. "I can't even run away," he said at the end. "I am watched all the time by the squire's men. See them over there at the corner?"

"Dear me," said the old woman. "This is a sad story. Mind you, laddie, you brought it on yourself. But this is Christmas Eve. Here, help me get my bag off my back. I will share my bread with you." She filled Jan's pockets with crusts of bread.

Jan was so happy! He thanked the kind old beggar woman and ran to a barn to celebrate his Christmas Eve.

The servants told the squire what they had seen.

"Bring Jan to me," demanded the squire.

Jan stood before his master. The squire said, "Seeing that the old beggar woman has taken pity upon you, I cannot remain hard-hearted. From today you may have potatoes. But there will be no bread for you until you harvest the wheat yourself."

Now Jan waited eagerly for the spring. Every day he went to look at the wheat and watch it grow.

At last the wheat was ready to be harvested. Jan hurried to the field and worked from dawn to dark. He enjoyed every minute of it. He was harvesting his own bread.

When Jan had threshed the wheat, he took it to the mill and had it ground into flour. Then

Mary baked him his first loaf of bread for many months. It was warm, crunchy, home-made bread, which smelled better than anything else on earth.

The squire cut off a crust and gave it to Jan.

"Here, my lad," he said kindly. "You have earned your crust of bread!"

Happy Jan

Jan remembered his father and the fields that needed a young man. He decided to return home.

He took his leave of the squire. He packed his knapsack and did not forget some bread. On his way home he sang. He was happy. His father welcomed him back with open arms.

For the rest of his life Jan worked his plot of land, sowing wheat and potatoes and making them grow. Sometimes, on Sundays, he would have meat to eat. Then he would think of the squire and of the big joints of meat. He would think sometimes of the woman and the crust of bread.

It goes without saying that he never wasted a piece of bread. He used to say, "Happy is the man who always has enough bread! I could tell you a a story about that."

AUTHOR

Andre Drucker was born in Czechoslovakia. During his boyhood, he listened to many folktales the people told. He says that *A Crust of Bread* was told to him by his grandmother.

Mr. Drucker left Czechoslovakia in 1938, when Germany took over his country during the Second World War. He went to live in England where he still lives. Besides writing, Mr. Drucker has opened a very successful coffee house near a college in Birmingham, England. He likes to meet the young people who come to his coffee house to paint, listen to music, and enjoy the good European food and coffee. Mr. Drucker also gives talks on radio and TV.

A Crust of Bread is one of the books in the Dolphin Series. Mr. Drucker has written two other Dolphin books as well: *Don Dorian* and *Tallula the Taxi.*

Beauty

by E-Yeh-Shure'

a young American Indian girl

Beauty is seen
In the sunlight,
The trees, the birds,
Corn growing and people working
Or dancing for their harvest.

Beauty is heard
In the night,
Wind sighing, rain falling,
Or a singer chanting
Anything in earnest.

Beauty is in yourself.
Good deeds, happy thoughts
That repeat themselves
In your dreams,
In your work,
And even in your rest.

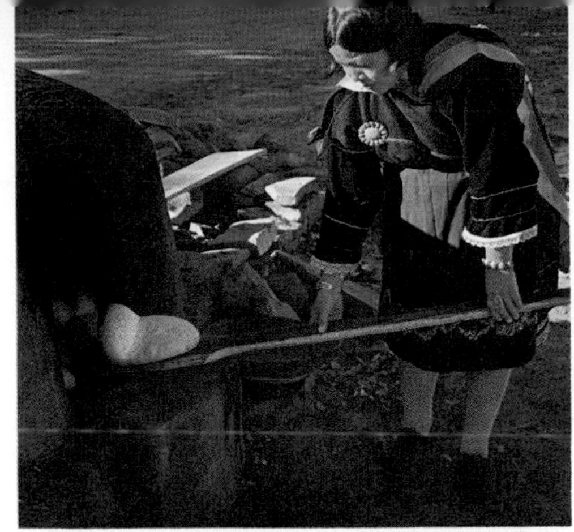

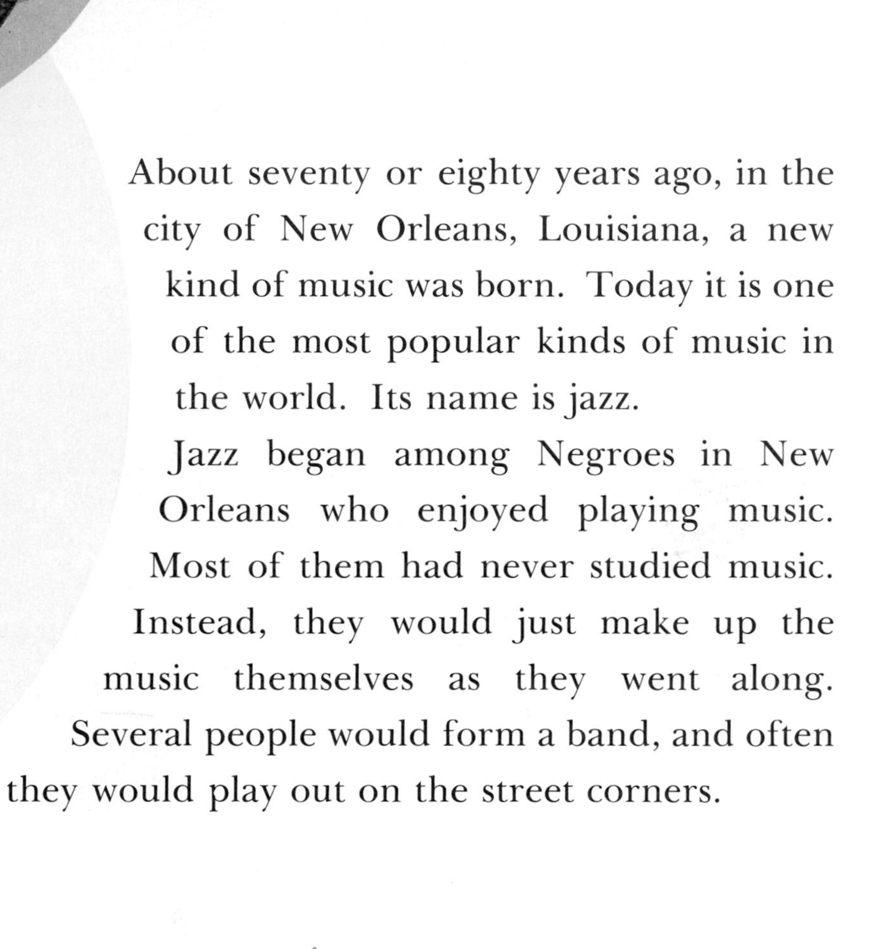

About seventy or eighty years ago, in the city of New Orleans, Louisiana, a new kind of music was born. Today it is one of the most popular kinds of music in the world. Its name is jazz.

Jazz began among Negroes in New Orleans who enjoyed playing music. Most of them had never studied music. Instead, they would just make up the music themselves as they went along. Several people would form a band, and often they would play out on the street corners.

JAZ

As the years went by, jazz became very popular in the rest of the United States and throughout the world. One of the people who did most to make this happen was Louis Armstrong.

Louis and his friends used to sing for pennies when they were little boys on the streets of New Orleans. Young Louis then learned to play the trumpet in a boys' band. He became so good at it that he was soon well known in New Orleans.

His big chance came when King Oliver, a bandleader Louis had always respected, asked him to come to Chicago to be part of his band. Louis Armstrong soon became one of the most popular musicians of all time, playing his trumpet in almost every part of the world.

One of the great jazz composers is a man named Edward Kennedy ("Duke") Ellington. Duke was born in Washington, D.C. He loved to play the piano his own way, but he never liked to take piano lessons. He used to skip the lessons to

play ball with the other boys! But even at a young age, he had unusual talent.

In his early teens, Duke worked at a soda fountain. It was then that he composed his first piece of music, "The Soda Fountain Rag." After that he decided to become a musician.

Duke became well known when he and his band began playing at the Cotton Club in New York. During this time he composed much of his most famous music. Duke often got ideas from things he saw every day. Once he was watching a neon sign blink on and off. Suddenly he began to compose a piece in his head to the rhythm, and later he wrote it down. One of his most famous works, "Harlem Airshaft," came from listening to the sounds in a tall apartment house in the city.

Jazz is America's gift to the world of music. Louis Armstrong, Duke Ellington, and many others have made it a wonderful gift indeed.

If you would like to learn more about jazz and musicians like Duke Ellington (shown here), there are many excellent books you can read. Two of these are The First Book of Jazz *by Langston Hughes and* Journey Into Jazz *by Nat Hentoff.*

Skill Lesson 3:

RECOGNIZING PARAGRAPH TOPICS

You know that almost everything you read is made up of groups of sentences that are called **paragraphs.** This arrangement of sentences in paragraphs can be a real help to you when you are reading to get some kind of information.

When a good writer starts to write a paragraph for a factual article, he has in mind just one point or idea that he wants the paragraph to tell about. He makes his first sentence say something about that one thing. Then he makes each of his other sentences say something about that same thing. By the time he has finished writing that paragraph, all the sentences in it say something about only one thing. We call that one thing the **topic** of the paragraph.

In the following paragraph, the sentences are numbered so that you can think about them easily later. As you read them now, try to decide what one thing all the sentences tell about.

> 1. Wherever people live, many of them have gardens. 2. Gardens may be big, or they may be small. 3. Some people have gardens mainly for beauty or fun. 4. They grow flowers like morning glories and roses in their gardens. 5. Other people use gardens mainly as a way to get fresh foods. 6. They grow things like melons, tomatoes, and squash.

Sentence 1 tells where *gardens* are found. Sentence 2 talks about the sizes of *gardens.* Sentence 3 tells one reason for having a *garden.* Sentence 4 tells what might be grown in a *garden* for that reason. Sentence 5 tells another reason for having a *garden.* Sentence 6 tells what might be grown in a *garden* for that reason. You can see that each sentence says something about the same thing, and that this one thing is gardens. That is why *gardens* is the topic of the paragraph.

To find out what the topic of a paragraph is, you must think what one thing all the sentences in that paragraph are talking about. Often you can do this quickly, right after you have read the paragraph just once. But sometimes you may have to study each sentence again to be sure.

When you do not know quickly what the topic of a paragraph is, do these things:

1. Read the first sentence again and think what it is talking about.
2. Do the same thing with each of the other sentences.
3. Then decide what one thing all the sentences are talking about. That one thing is the topic of the paragraph.

Whenever you read to get information, try to decide what the topics of the paragraphs are. Doing this can help you understand and remember what the paragraphs say.

Study the paragraph below and decide what its topic is.

> In the early days of the United States, many people lived in cabins. The cabins were made from logs that were fitted together to make the walls. Other logs were split and used to make the roof. Usually a cabin was small and had just one or two rooms. But

it was a place in which a family could stay warm and dry in the winter.

Which of the following topics is the topic of that paragraph?

1. How cabin roofs are made
2. The cabins of early settlers
3. Building cabin walls
4. The size of log cabins

Discussion

Help your class answer these questions:

1. What is meant by the topic of a paragraph?
2. Which of the four topics is the topic of the paragraph you just read? Why is each of the other topics *not* the topic of the paragraph?
3. If you cannot decide quickly what the topic of a paragraph is, what can you do to find out what the topic is?

On your own

Read the following paragraph to yourself and decide what its topic is:

Bananas are eaten and liked by people in just about every part of the world. Bananas have in them most of the things people need to eat to stay healthy. They are grown wherever the weather is always hot and wet. More bananas are grown in South America than anywhere else. They grow in bunches on leafstalks that are so tall they look like trees. Bananas are picked when they are still green. They become yellow and ripe on the way to the stores where you buy them.

Checking your work

Help your class decide what the topic of that paragraph is. If you are asked to do so, explain how you knew that one of the following was *not* the topic:

1. Why people eat bananas
2. How bananas are grown
3. When bananas are picked
4. Where bananas are grown

SUMMER

When summer blues the skies
And thrushes sing for hours,
And gold and orange butterflies
Float by like flying flowers . . .
Although I squint my eyes
The way a thinker does,
Somehow, I just can't realize
That winter ever was.

— KAYE STARBIRD

AS TO THE RESTLESS BROOK

Do you suppose the babbling brook
 Would stop and rest its head
If someone got a scoop and took
 The pebbles from its bed?

— JOHN KENDRICK BANGS

There once was a gentle young knight
Who would rather stay at home than fight.
"When I'm out," he'd explain,
"It commences to rain,
And my armor gets rusty and tight!"

– *Harriet Mandelbaum*

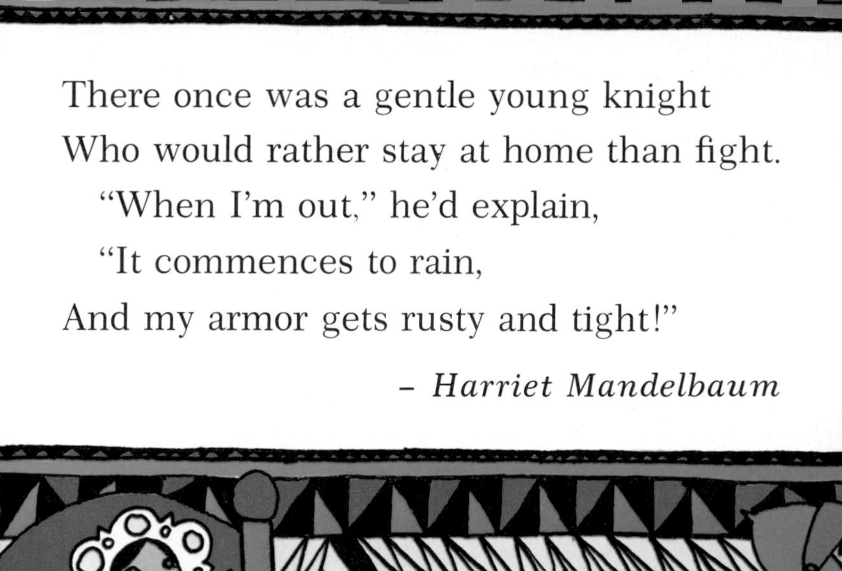

There was a young queen named Alice.
One day as she sat in the palace,
There came a big shake —
It was an earthquake —
Now the palace is sitting on Alice.

– *Barbara Clemons*

CAST	Innkeeper	The King
	His Wife	Attendant
	Hired Boy	

(The setting is an old inn. The innkeeper is sitting at a table. As the play opens, the innkeeper's wife rushes in.)

WIFE: Get up, husband. Have you not heard the news?

INNKEEPER: News? What news?

WIFE: I was just down at the village. I heard that the King is coming this way! Surely he will stop at our inn.

INNKEEPER: The King? He's coming this way? Are you sure?

WIFE: Indeed I am. He's coming soon. (*She grabs the broom.*) Hurry, we must clean. Where is that stupid servant boy?

INNKEEPER: He just stepped out to fetch a pail of water and some wood. Here he comes now. (*Hired boy enters with wood and water.*)

WIFE: (*To boy*) Here, Stupid! Don't just stand there. The King is coming! You must scrub the floor.

HIRED BOY: (*Putting down the wood and pail*) The King is coming? Here?

WIFE: Don't stand there and ask questions. Get to work! (*Hired boy begins to sweep.*)

INNKEEPER: We must have good bread for the King. I'll go to the baker's down the road.

WIFE: And we must have fresh eggs. I'll gather them. (*She turns to hired boy.*) Listen, boy. I'm putting you in charge of cleaning the inn. If any people stop here, tell them the King is coming and have them help you clean. Do you hear?

HIRED BOY: I hear. Anyone who comes must help. The King is coming.

WIFE: See that you have the inn spotless when we return, or you will lose your job. And a job is hard to come by these days. (*Hired boy gets to work quickly as innkeeper and wife leave.*)

HIRED BOY: I must go get the scrub pail and brushes. (*He leaves. King and Attendant enter.*)

ATTENDANT: Ah, what a cheerful inn, Your Majesty. Do sit down, Sire. We have had a long journey. I'm sure you are tired.

KING: Yes, it has been a long journey, but a good one. It has been nice to get away from all the fuss and ceremony. Not many people recognize me in these clothes. The peasants look so happy! I wish I could be a peasant, if only for a little while.

ATTENDANT: You are tired, Sire. Rest here while I tend to the horses. You'll feel better after you rest.

THE PEASANT'S GUIDE TO THE
KING DOM

(*Hired boy enters as attendant leaves.*)

HIRED BOY: Ah, I'm glad to see that someone has come. The innkeeper's wife said everyone must help to get ready for the King. He is coming this way very soon. So, my friend, please get ready to help me clean. The inn must be swept and scrubbed before the King comes.

KING: But — but — you don't know —

HIRED BOY: I don't know much, it's true. But there is no time for talk. Here, take this brush. I'll take the

other one. We must scrub the floor beneath that table. The King will sit there.

KING: But, my good man —

HIRED BOY: I am not your good man! I am the hired boy. Come, get to work, or I will lose my job! Hurry, there's not much time. We must work together.

KING: (*Smiling*) It is for the King, eh? Well, give me the brush. Just how do I go about this?

HIRED BOY: You are more stupid than I am! Here, get down like this. (*They kneel under table.*) Hold the brush like this. Scrub back and forth until the floor is clean. (*King begins to scrub.*) Harder! You must press hard. Ah, you learn fast. You're doing fine. I'm sure if the innkeeper's wife saw you, she would hire you on the spot. I'll put in a good word for you.

KING: Thank you! Your compliment does me good. (*Hired boy whistles.*) Must I whistle, too?

HIRED BOY: Oh, it's much easier to work when you whistle. (*King whistles while he works. They look at each other and smile as they work. Innkeeper and wife enter.*)

INNKEEPER: The baker has nice fresh bread.

WIFE: And I gathered plenty of eggs. We shall fix a fine meal for the King. Ah, I see the boy has help.

(*Goes to King*) Scrub well under the table, and hurry. The King will be here soon. (*Attendant enters.*)

ATTENDANT: Ah, good day. We stopped for a bite to eat and to rest on our way to the castle. (*Looks around*) But where is His Majesty, the King?

INNKEEPER: The King?

HIRED BOY: (*Looks up from under table*) No king here. Just me and this good man who is helping

me. (*Attendant gasps as he looks under table at King. The King looks up smiling and then gets up.*)

ATTENDANT: (*Bowing*) Your Majesty!

WIFE: What? The King!

INNKEEPER: Not the King!

HIRED BOY: Are you — are you the King?

KING: Ah, that I am. But for a short time you have made me a peasant. And a good one, you said!

WIFE: Oh, what have you done, you stupid boy?

INNKEEPER: Yes, what have you done to the King? We are very sorry, Your Majesty. That stupid boy knows nothing.

KING: You call him stupid?

WIFE: Indeed we do.

KING: (*Speaks to hired boy*) Stupid One, you have made me do a peasant's work, and I enjoyed it. Moreover, I can see that you do your own work very well. I would like you to come to my palace and be in charge of the cleaning. We shall call you KNIGHT STUPENDOUS!

HIRED BOY: Oh, thank you, Sire!

KING: And now, Knight Stupendous, will you order food for us? You shall sit at my right while we eat. (*King, Attendant, and hired boy sit at table.*)

HIRED BOY: (*To the woman*) Come, good woman. Bring us food and drink. We must eat and be on our way.

WIFE: Yes, sir! (*To husband*) Come, help me get food and drink. Don't stand there staring. Come! (*They rush out to get food.*)

ATTENDANT: (*Comes to front of stage and bows to audience*) That is the end of the play, my friends. (*Turns toward King and hired boy and raises his hand*) Long live His Majesty, the Peasant!

AUTHOR

Sally Werner was born in Finland, and she came to the United States when she was seven years old. Mrs. Werner first began writing when she worked with the Girl Scouts and wrote plays for their puppet shows. She then decided to try writing for children's magazines, and she is still doing this successfully.

Mrs. Werner also worked as a nurse. After her husband died, she moved to Florida. Besides writing for magazines, Mrs. Werner keeps busy as chairman of a neighborhood group that puts on plays.

There was a naughty boy
And a naughty boy was he.
He ran away to Scotland,
The people for to see.
But he found
That the ground
Was as hard,
That a yard
Was as long,
That a song
Was as merry,
That a cherry
Was as red,
That lead
Was as weighty,
That four-score
Was still eighty,
And a door was as wooden as in England.
So he stood in his shoes and he wondered,
He wondered, he wondered,
So he stood in his shoes and he wondered.

– *John Keats*

A RIDE ON HIGH

By CANDIDA PALMER

Tony awoke and remembered it was Saturday. Today he would ride the elevated to the game at his big cousin Charlie's school.

He listened for the rumble of the elevated trains passing back and forth on high tracks above his street. This morning he heard a wet, spattering noise as well. He jumped out of bed, ran to the window, and squeezed behind the window shade. Brr-r-r-snap! The shade flew up and flapped around the roller at the top.

"Oh, rain!" Tony groaned. Rain spoiled everything! "There'll be no game, so there'll be no ride on the el!"

A few minutes later, there was a knock at the door. It was Charlie.

"Will the rain stop?" Tony asked Charlie. Charlie was on the Roosevelt Junior High baseball lineup today.

"They haven't called off the game," Charlie said. "I'm going anyhow. There's practice first. Here . . ." He handed Tony two free passes for the game, for himself and for his best friend Chester. "And mind that you two little kids don't give me any trouble." Charlie put on his raincoat and raced out the door.

Tony watched at the window. By mid-morning the first watery sunshine sparkled on the shiny black street. He jingled the two quarters for his train fares in his pocket, just for luck. After lunch the ground was dry.

"Hurrah, we can ride the elevated!" Tony yelled. He ran all the way along his block and around the corner to Chester's house. Chester sat waiting on the steps.

"Have you got the passes and your money?" Chester demanded.

"Here, Chet, let's go!" Tony gave him one yellow pass and showed his two coins.

"I have an idea," Chester said on their way to the station at Fifty-second Street. "Together we have a dollar, right? Let's buy four tokens, two for our fares there and two to come back. Then there'll be change for candy."

At the newsstand under the stairs to the elevated, Chester studied the printed sign. "TOKENS: 4 for 90 cents," he read aloud.

They bought four shiny round brass tokens for the ride. The man gave them two nickels in change. Tony put his nickel into the slot of a candy machine. Out came a crunchy nut bar. Then Chester chose a caramel. They ran up the long iron stairs to the elevated station. There they each dropped one brass token into the slot of the turnstile. Click. The turnstile swung around and let them through to the train platform.

From the station Tony could see his house. Sparrows were splashing in a puddle on his roof. Today it was easy to find his window, because the shade was still tangled over the roller at the top!

Then Tony heard the train approach with a loud roar. It was rushing towards them like a silver monster. It stopped, and the doors slid open right where they stood. There were two empty seats together.

"Here we go!" Tony sang out. They were speeding along high above the playground now. The train stopped again. Tony counted the stops, four in all. He knew the stop for Roosevelt Junior High

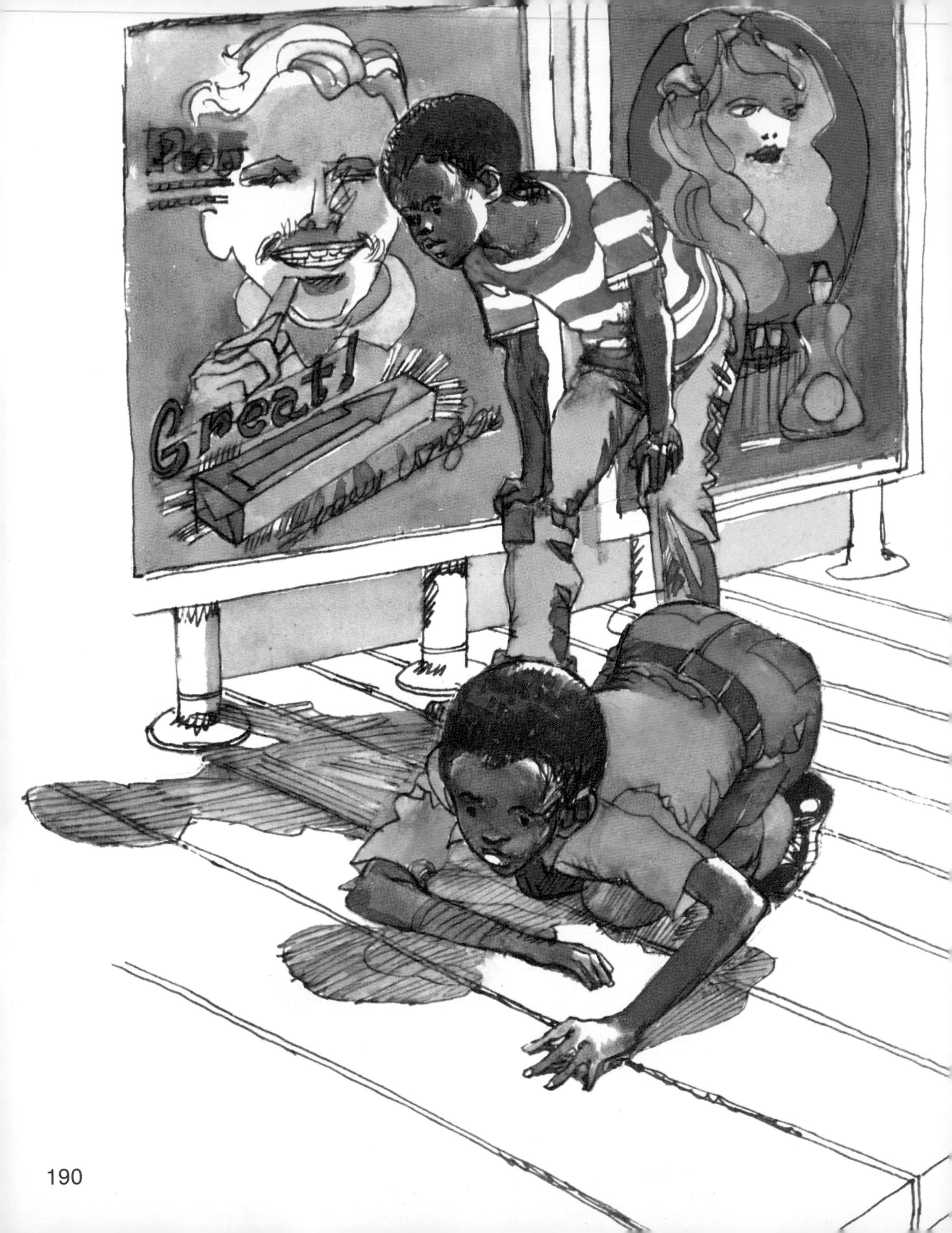
Great!

came right after the narrow-pointed church steeple with the clock.

"I see Charlie's school," Tony was first to shout. The train slowed down and stopped. Quickly they stepped off. From the elevated platform, they looked down on the school buildings and the large playing field.

Tony pulled his pass out of his pocket. Whoops! Clink! His token jumped out with it. It rolled along its edge. He put his foot out, fast. He slipped. The token disappeared through a crack in the platform. He heard a faint, distant clink as it hit somewhere below.

"My token's lost!" Tony gasped with fright. "How'll I get home?" he wailed.

"We'll have to find it," Chester said, but he didn't sound hopeful. "Why don't you go down and look for it? Then if you don't find it, maybe you can find Charlie."

"Oh, he won't like that," Tony said quickly. "We could phone home . . ."

"Can't phone with tokens. Only money's good in phones," Chester answered. "You go down and take my last token. You'll need it to get back up. Maybe you'll just happen to see Charlie . . ."

A Long Ride Home

Tony took Chester's token, walked slowly through the exit turnstile, and down the long iron stairs. He looked for the token below the platform. He looked under parked cars. He sighed. He would have to find Charlie.

There were crowds at each gate and all along the fence. The band started playing "O Say Can You See?" The game was about to begin, and Charlie was probably already in the outfield.

A gruff voice demanded Tony's pass. Then he was pushed along in a slow stream of tall people up into the high bleachers. The baseball diamond looked very far away, especially the outfield. Was that tall player Charlie? He couldn't tell.

Tony watched two innings. A cold lump settled in his stomach when he remembered his lost token, and Chester up on the elevated station. He stood up and struggled out through the crowded row of seats. At last he found an exit. He ran all the way around the big playing field back to the elevated. He didn't stop running until he reached the turnstile at the top of the stairs. He dropped Chester's token into the slot. It was their last.

Chester's eyes were fixed on the distant playing field.

"Home run!" Chester shouted, jumping up and down.

"I'm back, Chet," Tony said in a small voice. "Didn't meet Charlie . . ."

"Never mind. I figured something out while you were down," Chester answered, smiling. "We can't cross the platform here and take the train back, not without paying new tokens. But when I went fishing with Uncle Ben, we rode on and on till there was no more track. I figure the train has to turn around. It's a long way, but we'll get a long ride home."

"Is it farther than the subway?" Tony asked.

"Much farther!"

"Is it past the Zoo?"

"Much farther!"

"Is it past the swimming pool in the park? I've never been farther than the park on the Fourth of July . . ."

"Still farther. It's ALL the way, and we have to come back ALL the way on that track over there," Chester explained. "You scared?"

Tony didn't want to sound scared. He could hear a train coming. He pulled himself up as tall as he could and held his breath. The roar of the train grew very loud. It stopped. There was only a moment to change his mind.

"Let's go, Chet," he said in a hoarse voice. They stepped aboard. Their train roared away.

Tony waited for the place where the trees and houses suddenly grew tall beside the track. Then, as if the ground swallowed them, track and all, the train rushed into the subway tunnel. There were stations underground, with lights and candy machines. Tony had always liked the subway ride best. Today it was so dark and spooky. He put his face close against the train window. All he saw was what looked like another lit-up train, just like theirs, going along beside them. A ghost train?

"Wish we'd come out," Tony whispered.

"Me, too," Chester agreed.

At last flashes of bright light shone between the big steel uprights. Tony closed his eyes. When he opened them, the train was climbing out of the dark, spooky tunnel into the bright sunshine, up to its elevated tracks. Now they could see where they were going. Tony watched for the ZOO sign, with the animal pictures. He also knew the park stop. The train kept going and going. Rows of chimneys were flashing by. Was there no end to this big city? Tony hoped the train would remember to turn around!

They stopped again. Every single passenger left the train and hurried off. Tony blinked his eyes. A big smile was spreading over Chester's face.

"I knew it! We're here!" Chester shouted and ran to the door. He laughed and jumped up and down. "Look, Tony! There comes a turned-around train, all ready to take off for home!"

It was still empty. Tony and Chester chose the very best seats. They were impatient for the motor of the train to start up and the doors to close.

"We're off!" they yelled together. They were going in the opposite direction now. They were on their way home!

It didn't seem long before the elevated train slowed down and the houses grew tall beside it.

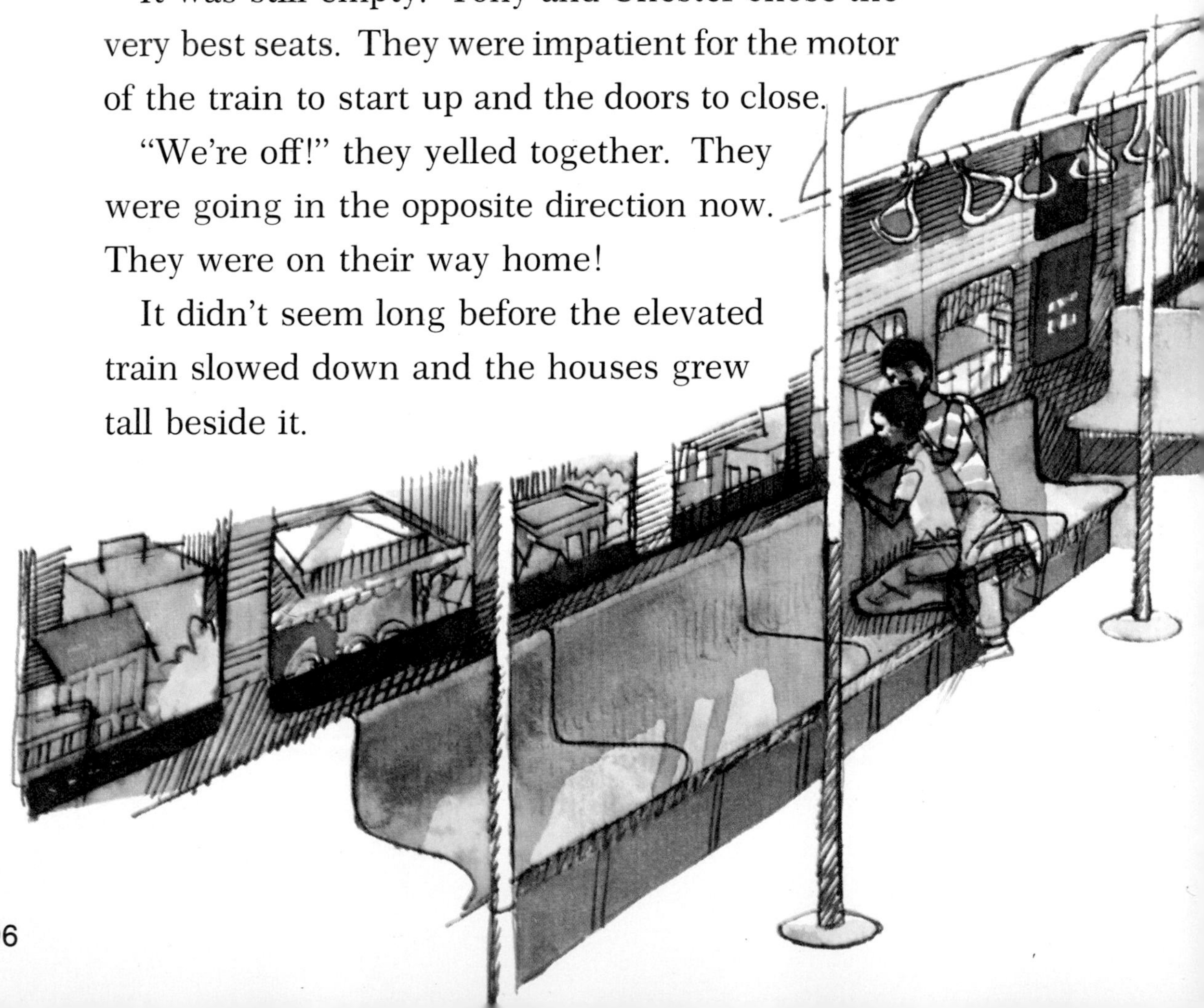

Whoosh! They roared through the magic subway tunnel again. Whoosh! Out they came!

"Roosevelt Junior High!" Chester called out. "See, everyone's gone home. Who do you reckon won the game?"

"Don't know . . . and don't care . . . This long ride home is best of all," Tony said. He laughed. "Chet, let's save quarters again and go for another ride. And it won't feel the least bit scary, 'cause it's a homecoming elevated, too!"

AUTHOR

The idea for *A Ride on High* came to Candida Palmer one Thanksgiving Day, as she and her family were riding the elevated in Philadelphia. They were riding to the end of the line in order to have Thanksgiving dinner with the Palmer grandparents. Crystal, Mrs. Palmer's daughter, was so excited with the long ride that another passenger turned to her and said, "Honey, is this the *first* time you've ever been on the elevated?" Mrs. Palmer then decided that children might enjoy reading a story about an elevated.

Mrs. Palmer came to the United States from New Zealand, where she grew up. She began to write stories for children when her own son and daughter, Logan and Crystal, started school. Her husband is a teacher in a college in Ohio. Mrs. Palmer has also written *Snowstorm Before Christmas.*

E is the escalator
   That gives an elegant ride.
You step on the stair
With an easy air
   And up and up you glide.
It's nicer than scaling ladders
   Or scrambling 'round a hill,
For you climb and climb
But all the time
   You're really standing still.

– Phyllis McGinley

TWO MAGIC NUMBERS

1.

Did you know that 99 is a magic number? No matter what number you use in the problem described below, your answer will be 99.

1. Write down any number that has two figures, as long as the two figures are different:	37
2. Now write the number backwards:	73
3. Subtract the smaller number from the larger one:	36
4. Write this number backwards:	63
5. Add the third and fourth numbers, and you'll always get:	99

2.

Another magic number is 1089. This trick is very much like the 99 trick, except that numbers with three figures are used. Below is an example.

1. Write down any number that has three figures, as long as the first and third figures are different:	218
2. Write this number backwards:	812
3. Subtract the smaller number from the larger one:	594
4. Write this number backwards:	495
5. Add the third and fourth numbers, and you'll always get:	1089

Marco Comes Late

by DR. SEUSS

1.

"Young man!" said Miss Block,
"It's eleven o'clock!
This school begins promptly at 8:45.
Why, *this* is a terrible time to arrive!
Why didn't you come just as fast as you could?
What *IS* your excuse? It had better be good!"
        Marco looked at the clock.
        Then he looked at Miss Block.
"Excuse?" Marco stuttered.
        "Er . . . well . . . well, you see
Er . . . Well, it's like this . . .
        Something happened to me.

2.

"This morning, Miss Block,
        when I left home for school,
I hurried off early according to rule.
I said, when I started at quarter past eight,
I *must* not, I *will* not, I *shall* not be late!

I'll be the first pupil to be in my seat.
Then *Bang*!
Something happened on Mulberry Street!

3.

"I heard a strange 'peep' and I took a quick look
And you know what I saw
with the look that I took?

A bird laid an egg on my 'Rithmetic Book!

I couldn't believe it, Miss Block, but it's true!
I stopped and I didn't quite know what to do.
I didn't dare run, and I didn't dare walk.
I didn't dare yell, and I didn't dare talk.
I didn't dare sneeze, and I didn't dare cough.
Because, if I did, it would knock the egg off.

So I stood there stock-still, and it worried me pink.
Then my feet got quite tired,
and I sat down to think.

4.

"And while I was thinking
down there on the ground,
I saw something move, and I heard a loud sound
Of a worm who was having a fight with his wife.
The most terrible fight that I've heard in my life!
The worm he was yelling,
'That boy should not wait!
He *must* not, he *dare* not, he *shall* not be late!
That boy ought to smash that egg off his head.'
Then the wife of the worm shouted back — and *she* said,
'To break that dear egg would be terribly cruel.
An egg's more important than going to school.
That egg is that mother bird's pride and her joy.
If he smashes that egg,
he's the world's meanest boy!'

5.

"And while the worms argued
'bout what I should do
A couple big cats started arguing, too!
'You listen to me!' I heard one of them say.

'If this boy doesn't go on to school right away,
Miss Block will be frightfully, horribly mad.
If the boy gets there late, she will punish the lad!'
Then the other cat snapped,
        'I don't care if she does.
This boy must not move!' So I stayed where I was
With the egg on my head,
        and my heart full of fears
And the shouting of cats and of worms in my ears.

6.

"Then, while I lay wondering
        when all this would stop,
The egg on my book burst apart with a *POP!*
And out of the pieces of red and white shell
Jumped a strange brand-new bird,
        and he said with a yell,
'I thank you, young fellow,
        you've been simply great.

But, now that I'm hatched,
you no longer need wait.

I'm sorry I kept you till 'leven o'clock.
It's really my fault. You tell *that* to Miss Block.
I wish you good luck, and I bid you good day.'
That's what the bird said. Then he fluttered away.
And *then* I got here just as fast as I could,
And that's my excuse and I think it's quite good."

7.

Miss Block didn't speak for a moment or two.
Her eyes looked at Marco
and looked him clean through.
Then she smiled.
"That's a very good tale, if it's true.
Did *all* of those things *really* happen to you?"

"Er . . . well," answered Marco
with sort of a squirm.
"Not *quite* all, I guess. But I *did* see a worm."

AUTHOR

Theodor Seuss Geisel, who writes under the name "Dr. Seuss," has long been a favorite author with boys and girls. He feels that above all, reading should be *fun.* The popularity of his books proves that many people agree with him.

Dr. Seuss was born in Massachusetts and wanted to be a history teacher. But when his cartoons became successful, he turned to writing and illustrating for a living. He first sold cartoons to magazines and then made movie cartoons. One of them, "Gerald McBoing-Boing," won an Academy Award in 1950 as the best movie cartoon of that year.

The first book for children by Dr. Seuss, *And To Think That I Saw It on Mulberry Street,* was an instant success. Since then he has written many, many books, such as *Fox in Socks, Horton Hatches the Egg, The Cat in the Hat,* and *The Cat in the Hat Comes Back.*

TWO WEEKS OLD AND ON HIS OWN

Peek was a little field mouse. His first day on his own was the beginning of a most unusual life for a mouse.

Peek was down by the river bank. Some children were making toy boats from pine bark. Peek stepped into one of the boats, and the next thing he knew he was floating away from the bank. Now the strong wind had blown the boat out into the middle of the river.

by *VITALI BIANKI*

The little mouse was only two weeks old. He knew nothing about life. He didn't know how to search for food, hide from his enemies, or find shelter from wind and water. He didn't even know that he had enemies. But worst of all, he was unaware of the unseen dangers that were all around him.

One of those dangers was circling above him right now. A white gull had spied him. Soon Peek heard a whole flight of gulls screaming. They settled down on the water and paddled up alongside the little boat.

Peek was in trouble! What he didn't know was that a fish had seen the gulls and had come up to the surface. The fish was waiting for the gulls to tip the boat over, so that he could snap up the mouse in his sharp jaws. As the gulls came toward him, Peek closed his eyes.

Just then a fish hawk appeared overhead. Seeing the boat, the mouse, the gulls, and the waiting fish,

the hawk swooped down. With the tip of his wing he brushed the boat, turning it over. When the hawk flew off, he had the fish, and Peek was in the water.

Peek went down. Then he came up. And somewhere in between he learned to swim. Paddling furiously with all four feet, he swam to the wooden boat and clung to it with his teeth. A little later the boat crashed into some rocks and was flung upon a sandy shore. Peek leaped for the bushes.

He was soaked. Also he was very hungry. To find food, Peek had to leave his hiding place beneath the bush. As long as he could hear the screams of the gulls from the river, he was afraid to leave. So there he stayed, hungry and miserable. He was there in the afternoon. He was there in the evening. He was there when the sun went down and the birds went to roost. Everything became so quiet that he could hear nothing but water lapping on the shore. Only then, under cover of darkness, did he dare to leave his hiding place.

Even then he was cautious. Every few steps, he stopped and looked around him. There was no one. Growing bolder, he began to roll in the grass like a small dark ball, biting at the stems and leaves. No juice came from them. He began to tear them apart with his teeth. Suddenly the juice from a stalk came splashing all over his face. It was sweet and cool. Finishing that stalk, he searched for others. Peek was so busy searching for food that he did not notice anything going on around him.

Soon the moon came out. On all sides of him, Peek could hear faint rustlings and murmurs. Things were stirring in the bushes and in the grass.

The hungry little mouse went on eating. The tips of the stalk turned out to be delicious. Suddenly he heard a strange sound. Instantly his jaws stopped moving. His ears shot up. He listened.

"Bump bump." What a strange sound! "Bump bump." Something was hopping in the grass, straight in his direction. Peek thought of the bush and his hiding place. "Bump bump." Now the sound was behind him. "Bump bump." Now it was all around him, close by. Then there was a last "bump" right in

front of his nose. He found himself face to face with a goggle-eyed little frog who stared at him. Peek stared back. And there they sat, staring at one another in amazement.

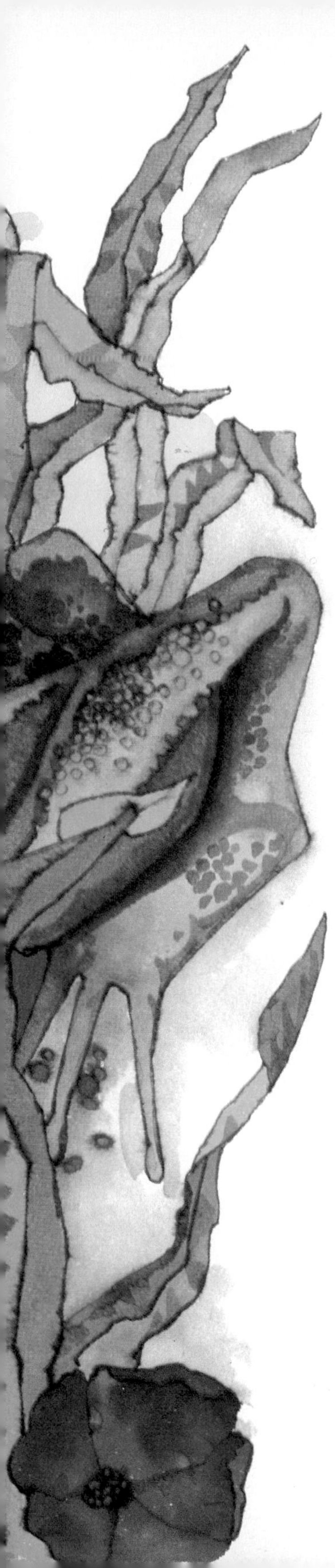

All around them the "bump bump" continued. Then there was a faint, swift, rustling sound in the grass. Peek, still staring at the frog, saw a silvery black snake slide up behind the frog. The snake struck. The frog disappeared into its mouth.

Peek fled.

He leaped for the high safety of a bush and crawled to the topmost limb. There, perched like a bird, he spent the rest of the night wide awake. All around him, until dawn, he could hear stirrings and rustlings in the grass.

In spite of the dangers around him, Peek was making progress. He had learned the secret of finding food. Now, if he could just find a way to protect himself from his enemies, he would be a happier mouse. If he had lived with other mice, this problem would not have been so serious. Mice look out for one another. When a field mouse senses danger, he makes a whistling sound, and the others run for safety.

But Peek was alone. If there were other mice in this dangerous world, he hadn't seen them. He could go look for them. Right away he started down from the bush where he had spent the night. Halfway down he turned quickly and ran back up again. He had remembered the snake.

Peek felt safer up there. For all he knew, the ground was covered with snakes, all of them waiting to pounce on him. If only he could travel above the ground! If he could just jump from bush to bush! If . . . And then Peek, looking around him, discovered his tail!

It was an amazing discovery, and a very useful one. His tail was long and could curl itself around twigs and small limbs. Trying it out, he curled his tail around a tiny branch and lowered himself to another. Then he leaped across to another bush, curled his tail around a limb, and swung through the air like a baby monkey to still another bush. No snake could get him now. For three straight nights, Peek traveled from bush to bush.

But finally the bushes ended, and one morning the little mouse looked out across a meadow. He was very hungry, and the meadow was filled with good things to eat. Boldly he climbed down from the bush in the bright sunshine and started digging for food. It was a dry meadow, and there seemed to be no snakes. But, though Peek didn't know it, there were other dangers just as deadly.

One of them was watching him right now.

It was a small bird hanging motionless in the air. Its wings were fluttering so rapidly that they did not

seem to be moving at all. This was a trembler, a bird about the size of a pigeon, only not so fat. Peek saw the trembler. It didn't seem dangerous. The bird just hovered in the air. Besides, the hungry little mouse had dug up some delicious beetle eggs and was sitting up on his hind legs, holding them in his fore-paws and eating. The tiny white spot on Peek's breast shone bright against the brown earth.

It was the white spot which caught the sharp eyes of the trembler. Down he swooped, as silent as an arrow. Only then did Peek realize that the trembler was his enemy. But by then it was too late to run for the bushes. Peek flung himself flat against the ground and lay still, his heart pounding wildly.

The trembler missed him. Back into the sky the bird flashed, hovering motionlessly above. But now

no tiny white spot could be seen. Where it had been, there was only the color of brown earth. Peek's color blended perfectly with the ground. Though the bird looked and looked, it could see nothing. And yet, little Peek was lying there all the time, his heart hammering.

A moment later a green grasshopper jumped from the grass. The trembler darted, grabbed it, and flew away. Peek's enemy had gone.

The little mouse had learned two amazing things. One was that he had a most useful tail. He could also make himself invisible to even the sharpest eyes.

Peek had many other exciting adventures before he finally found a safe place to live. You can read about them in the book, Peek the Piper, *by Vitali Bianki.*

AUTHOR

Vitali Bianki was born in Russia. He has always been interested in nature and enjoys writing true-to-life animal stories such as *Peek the Piper.* He also writes folktales for boys and girls. Other books of Mr. Bianki's that you may enjoy are *Galinka, the Wild Goose* and *How I Wanted to Pour Salt on a Rabbit's Tail and Other Stories.*

Skill Lesson 4:

GETTING HELP FROM COMMAS

You know that a **period** (.) usually says, "Come to a full stop here before you go on to the next sentence." You also know that a **question mark** (?) at the end of a sentence tells you to read that sentence as if you were asking a question. And you know that an **exclamation mark** (!) tells you that the word or words before it were said loudly or with strong feeling. We call such marks **punctuation marks.** They tell you something about how a sentence would sound if you heard some-one saying it.

A **comma** (,) is another punctuation mark that you will often see in your reading. A comma usually says, "Slow down and pause slightly here before you go on to the next word." Doing that whenever you see a comma can help you in your reading.

As you read Sentence 1 below, see if you can decide what Bobby said he'd had to eat at a friend's house.

1. Bobby said he'd eaten fruit salad cheese biscuits beef pie applesauce cake nuts and lemonade.

Did Bobby have fruit and salad, or fruit salad? Did he have cheese and biscuits, or cheese biscuits? Did he have beef and pie, or beef pie? Did he have applesauce and cake, or applesauce cake? You can't tell, can you?

Read Sentence 2 below, and see if the added commas help you know quickly just what Bobby had to eat.

2. Bobby said he'd eaten fruit salad, cheese biscuits, beef pie, applesauce, cake, nuts, and lemonade.

Now you can see that Bobby had seven different things to eat or drink.

If you said that sentence aloud to tell someone what Bobby had eaten, would you make a pause between *fruit* and *salad?* Of course not! What would you do to make it clear that he'd had applesauce and cake instead of a special kind of cake called applesauce cake? You'd make a little pause between the words *applesauce* and *cake,* wouldn't you? You'd make a little pause wherever there is a comma in that sentence. Those commas stand for the little pauses or hesitations you would make in saying that sentence.

You can see that noticing those commas and thinking a little pause for each one helps you understand the sentence. Doing that will let you know what things Bobby had and will help you keep those things apart in your mind. Often you will find such lists of things, people, or ideas in sentences. When you do, just think a little pause for each comma. Then you will know what the different things are.

As you read Sentence 3 below, see if you can tell whether Terry is a boy, a girl, or a pet.

3. I took Terry to the park.

You have no idea who Terry is, do you? The speaker, though, could tell you who Terry is by adding another sentence, like this:

4. Terry is my younger brother.

Or he could have said this sentence in the first place:

5. I took Terry, my younger brother, to the park.

By adding the words "my younger brother" to Sentence 3, the speaker could make one sentence do

the job of two. Notice that when those words are added, a comma is placed before and after them to tell the reader to make a little pause for each one so that he will know that those words are about Terry.

When a group of words is set off from the rest of a sentence by a comma or a pair of commas, those words very often tell something special about the naming word that comes just before or just after them. Only one comma is needed, of course, when the group of words comes at the beginning or end of a sentence:

6. A slow-moving and good-natured animal, the porcupine is well protected by thousands of sharp spines loosely fixed to its skin.
7. One of the fastest runners of all animals is the ostrich, the largest bird known today.

Notice that if the group of words set off by commas had been left out, you would still have a perfectly good sentence. You can see that you have no trouble understanding those sentences if you just think a little pause when you come to each comma.

As you read Sentence 8 below, think what the word between the commas does:

8. Dad will give us a ride, Jim, if you're ready now.

Is the word *Jim* the name of one person in a list of names of people? Does the word *Jim* tell something

special about the word *ride?* No, it names the person to whom someone is talking, doesn't it? When you see a name of someone or something set off from the rest of a sentence by a comma or a pair of commas, remember that the name may be telling you who is being spoken to. Usually, such a name and the words used with it will appear within **quotation marks** (" ") to show that someone is talking.

Decide who is being spoken to in these sentences:

9. "Ken, can you help me?" asked Mother.
10. "Where are you going, Pete?" asked Bill.

Now look at the next two sentences. They are just alike except that one has two commas and the other has only one. See if you can decide what the difference in meaning is between the two sentences. Be sure to pause a bit when you come to a comma.

11. Alice, the girl next door, is the same age as you.
12. Alice, the girl next door is the same age as you.

Discussion

Help your class answer these questions:

1. What do we call marks like periods, question marks, exclamation marks, and commas? How can such marks help you in reading?
2. Why is Sentence 2 easier to read than Sentence 1? Where should the commas have been if Bobby had had fruit and salad, cheese and biscuits, beef and pie, and applesauce?
3. Sometimes a group of words coming next to a naming word is set off from the rest of the sentence by a comma or a pair of commas. What does such a group of words often do? What two sentences could you easily make out of Sentence 6? Out of Sentence 7?
4. Sometimes a person's name is not in a list of names but is set off from the rest of a sentence by a comma or a pair of commas. Why? Who was being spoken to in Sentence 9? In Sentence 10? What are quotation marks?
5. What is the difference in meaning between Sentences 11 and 12?

On your own

As you read the paragraph that follows, remember to think a little pause for every comma. Decide why each word or group of words set off by a comma or a pair of commas was set off that way from the rest of the sentence.

> Mark wanted a baseball, glove, and bat for his birthday. His mother let him have a party and invite five of his friends, all of whom were boys that lived nearby and were in his class at school. He was disappointed when Dick, his best friend, could not come. Jim, Frank, Larry, and Tom arrived right on time. The boys played games that Mrs. Blake, Mark's mother, had planned. Each one of the guests received a prize, a model airplane kit. The boys enjoyed birthday cake, ice cream, and chocolate milk. "It's time to open your presents, Mark," said Mrs. Blake when the boys had finished eating. Usually a very calm boy, Mark jumped up and down with delight when he found a ball, glove, and bat in the package from his parents. Mark thought it really was a perfect birthday, just about the best he could possibly have had!

Checking your work

If you are asked to do so, read one of the sentences in the paragraph above, and explain how the commas helped you to understand the meaning.

THE LEAF PILE

by Kaye Starbird

I raked the leaves today, and after a while
I piled them near the steps in a jumping pile;
And later on, with supper and homework ended,
As Mother sat in the dining room and mended,
I said: "The moon is shining under the eaves.
Tonight's a perfect night for jumping in leaves.
Too bad you're old and busy with socks and sleeves."

My mother squinted down at a stocking heel
And answered, "Age isn't age. It's how you feel;
And now I'm feeling sick of this mending box.
Tonight's no night for working on sleeves and socks."
And, raising the blind to get the moon in sight,
She seemed to ponder a bit and said, "You're right.
It *is* a perfect jump-in-the-leaf-pile night."
And then she closed her box so loudly it thumped,
And both of us went out on the steps and jumped.

THE HERONS ON BO ISLAND

The herons on Bo Island
  Stand solemnly all day;
Like lean old men together
  They hump their shoulders gray.
Oh, I wish I could get near them
  To hear the things they say!

They turn up their coat collars
  And stand so gloomily;
And somehow, as I watch them,
  It always seems to me
That in their trouser pockets
  Their wrinkled hands must be.

But if I venture near them
  They look at me in doubt,
And with great wings loose-flapping
  They circle round about,
Their long legs hanging downwards
  Their slim necks all stretched out.

If I stood on Bo Island
  As gloomily as they,
And ruffled up my collar
  And hid my hands away,
It might be they would join me
  And I'd hear the things they say.

– *Elizabeth Shane*

From

WINNIE-THE-POOH

by A. A. MILNE

In Which Pooh and Piglet Go Hunting and Nearly Catch a Woozle

The Piglet lived in a very grand house in the middle of a beech-tree, and the beech-tree was in the middle of the forest, and the Piglet lived in the middle of the house. Next to his house was a piece of broken board which had: "TRESPASSERS W" on it. When Christopher Robin asked the Piglet what it meant, he said it was his grandfather's name, and had been in the family for a long time. Christopher Robin said you *couldn't* be called Trespassers W, and Piglet said yes, you could, because his grandfather was, and it was short for Trespassers Will, which was short of Trespassers William. And his grandfather had had two names in case he lost one — Trespassers after an uncle, and William after Trespassers.

"I've got two names," said Christopher Robin carelessly.

"Well, there you are, that proves it," said Piglet.

One fine winter's day when Piglet was brushing away the snow in front of his house, he happened to look up, and there was Winnie-the-Pooh. Pooh was walking round and round in a circle, thinking of something else, and when Piglet called to him, he just went on walking.

"Hallo!" said Piglet. "What are *you* doing?"

"Hunting," said Pooh.

"Hunting what?"

"Tracking something," said Winnie-the-Pooh very mysteriously.

"Tracking what?" said Piglet, coming closer.

"That's just what I ask myself. I ask myself, What?"

"What do you think you'll answer?"

"I shall have to wait until I catch up with it," said Winnie-the-Pooh. "Now, look there." He pointed to the ground in front of him. "What do you see there?"

"Tracks," said Piglet. "Paw-marks." He gave a little squeak of excitement. "Oh, Pooh! Do you think it's a — a — a Woozle?"

"It may be," said Pooh. "Sometimes it is, and sometimes it isn't. You never can tell with paw-marks."

With these few words he went on tracking, and Piglet, after watching him for a minute or two, ran after him. Winnie-the-Pooh had come to a sudden stop, and was bending over the tracks in a puzzled sort of way.

"What's the matter?" asked Piglet.

"It's a very funny thing," said Bear, "but there seem to be *two* animals now. This — whatever-it-was — has been joined by another — whatever-it-is — and the two of them are now proceeding in company. Would you mind coming with me, Piglet, in case they turn out to be Hostile Animals?"

Piglet scratched his ear in a nice sort of way, and said that he had nothing to do until Friday, and would be delighted to come, in case it really *was* a Woozle.

"You mean, in case it really is two Woozles," said Winnie-the-Pooh, and Piglet said that anyhow he had nothing to do until Friday. So off they went together.

There was a small spinney of larch trees just here, and it seemed as if the two Woozles, if that is what they were, had been going round this spinney; so round this spinney went Pooh and Piglet after them; Piglet passing the time by telling Pooh what his Grandfather Trespassers W had done to Remove Stiffness after Tracking, and how his Grandfather Trespassers W had suffered in his later years from Shortness of Breath, and other matters of interest, and Pooh wondering what a Grandfather was like, and if perhaps this was Two Grandfathers they were after now, and, if so, whether he would be allowed to take one home and keep it, and what Christopher Robin would say. And still the tracks went on in front of them. . . .

Suddenly Winnie-the-Pooh stopped, and pointed excitedly in front him. "*Look*!"

"*What*?" said Piglet, with a jump. And then, to show that he hadn't been frightened, he jumped up and down once or twice in an exercising sort of way.

"The tracks!" said Pooh. *"A third animal has joined the other two!"*

"Pooh!" cried Piglet. "Do you think it is another Woozle?"

"No," said Pooh, "because it makes different marks. It is either Two Woozles and one, as it might be, Wizzle, or Two, as it might be, Wizzles and one, if so it is, Woozle. Let us continue to follow them."

So they went on, feeling just a little anxious now, in case the three animals in front of them were of Hostile Intent. And Piglet wished very much that his Grandfather T. W. were there, instead of elsewhere, and Pooh thought how nice it would be if they met Christopher Robin suddenly but quite accidentally, and only because he liked Christopher Robin so much. And then, all of a sudden, Winnie-the-Pooh stopped again, and licked the tip of his nose in a cooling manner, for he was feeling more hot and anxious than ever in his life before. *There were four animals in front of them!*

"Do you see, Piglet? Look at their tracks! Three, as it were, Woozles, and one, as it was, Wizzle. *Another Woozle has joined them!*"

And so it seemed to be. There were the tracks; crossing over each other here, getting muddled up with each other there; but, quite plainly every now and then, the tracks of four sets of paws.

"I *think*," said Piglet, when he had licked the tip of his nose too, and found that it brought very little comfort, "I *think* that I have just remembered something. I have just remembered something that I forgot to do yesterday and shan't be able to do tomorrow. So I suppose I really ought to go back and do it now."

"We'll do it this afternoon, and I'll come with you," said Pooh.

"It isn't the sort of thing you can do in the afternoon," said Piglet quickly. "It's a very particular morning thing, that has to be done in the morning, and, if possible, between the hours of — What would you say the time was?"

"About twelve," said Winnie-the-Pooh, looking at the sun.

"Between, as I was saying, the hours of twelve

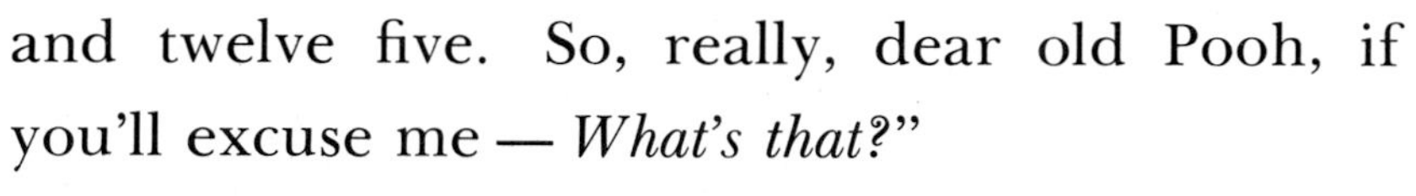

and twelve five. So, really, dear old Pooh, if you'll excuse me — *What's that?*"

Pooh looked up at the sky, and then, as he heard the whistle again, he looked up into the branches of a big oak-tree, and then he saw a friend of his.

"It's Christopher Robin," he said.

"Ah, then you'll be all right," said Piglet.

"You'll be quite safe with *him.* Good-by," and he trotted off home as quickly as he could, very glad to be Out of All Danger again.

Christopher Robin came slowly down his tree.

"Silly old Bear," he said, "what *were* you doing? First you went round the spinney twice by yourself, and then Piglet ran after you and you went round again together, and then you were just going round a fourth time — "

"Wait a moment," said Winnie-the-Pooh, holding up his paw.

He sat down and thought, in the most thoughtful way he could think. Then he fitted his paw into one of the Tracks . . . and then he scratched his nose twice, and stood up.

"Yes," said Winnie-the-Pooh.

"I see now," said Winnie-the-Pooh.

"I have been Foolish and Deluded," said he, "and I am a Bear of No Brain at All."

"You're the Best Bear in All the World," said Christopher Robin soothingly.

"Am I?" said Pooh hopefully. And then he brightened up suddenly.

"Anyhow," he said, "it is nearly Luncheon Time."

So he went home for it.

AUTHOR

A. A. Milne began to write *Winnie-the-Pooh* as he watched his own son, Christopher Robin, at play. The real Christopher Robin had a stuffed bear named Winnie-the-Pooh, and Mr. Milne enjoyed writing about them. He also added other animals such as Piglet, Eeyore the donkey, and Kanga and Baby Roo. His four books about Christopher Robin and his animal friends are among the best-loved books in the world. *Winnie-the-Pooh* and *The House at Pooh Corner* are collections of stories. *When We Were Very Young* and *Now We Are Six* are books of poems.

A problem arose when these books first became famous. People became excited when they learned that A. A. Milne really had a young son named Christopher Robin. They began to write letters to the little boy, and some even came to the Milne house just to see him! Mr. Milne grew worried that his son would become spoiled by all this attention. The author became so upset about this that he decided not to write any more Christopher Robin books.

A. A. Milne was born in London in 1882. For many years, he was an assistant editor of *Punch,* a British humor magazine. He also wrote many plays, poems, and stories for grown-ups. But he is remembered most for his Christopher Robin books. Although Mr. Milne died in 1956, these books live on and are as popular as ever.

MORE BOOKS TO ENJOY

ALL EXCEPT SAMMY, *by Gladys Yessayan Cretan.*

Sammy feels left out because he is the only one in his family with no musical talent. Then he discovers that he is talented in other ways.

THE BIG SNOW, *by Berta and Elmer Hader.*

This Caldecott medal winner tells how animals prepare for winter in the forest.

BUFFALO BILL, *by Ingri and Edward P. d'Aulaire.*

This is one of many fine books about the lives of famous people written by the d'Aulaires.

THE COUNTERFEIT TACKLE, *by Matt Christopher.*

When Corky has to miss his team's football game, his identical twin brother Buzz agrees to play in his place. The only problem is that Buzz knows almost nothing about football!

THE GREAT GEPPY, *by William Pène du Bois.*

In this one, a red and white striped horse is the detective who solves the mystery of some stolen circus money.

HIGGLETY PIGGLETY POP!, *by Maurice Sendak.*

A dog named Jennie, bored with her life, runs away and becomes a star in the Mother Goose Theatre.

Fantasia

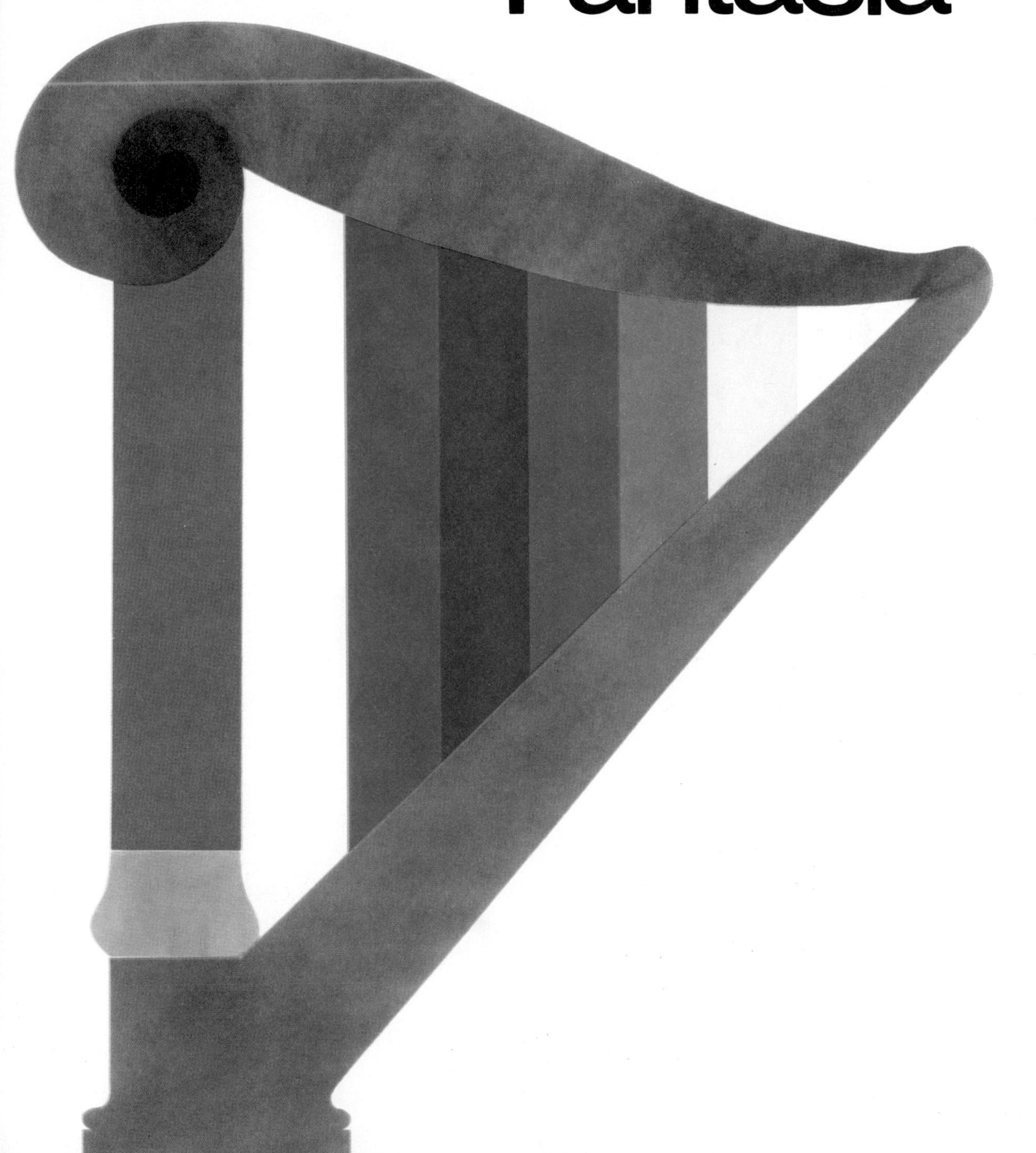

FANTASIA

A TIME TO TALK 239
by Robert Frost

CAMEL IN THE SEA 240
by Lee Garrett Goetz

THE CAMEL *and* THE DUCK 263
by Ogden Nash

VISITORS 264
by Harry Behn

BRAVE KATE SHELLEY 265
by Louis Wolfe

Skill Lesson 5: MAKING MENTAL PICTURES 277

WIND SONG 281
by Lilian Moore

COMMANDS 282
by Harriet Carlson

THE CASE OF THE MYSTERIOUS TRAMP 284
by Donald J. Sobol

TO BE ANSWERED IN OUR NEXT ISSUE 295

RUPERT PIPER BECOMES A HERO 296
by Ethelyn Parkinson

Skill Lesson 6: RECOGNIZING THE POWER OF WORDS 309

WE MUST BE POLITE 314
by Carl Sandburg

DESERT TRADERS 316
by Iona S. Hiser

WHAT IS GREEN? 320
by Mary O'Neill

A Story Treasure from MISCHIEVOUS MEG 322
by Astrid Lindgren

BIBLIOGRAPHY 346

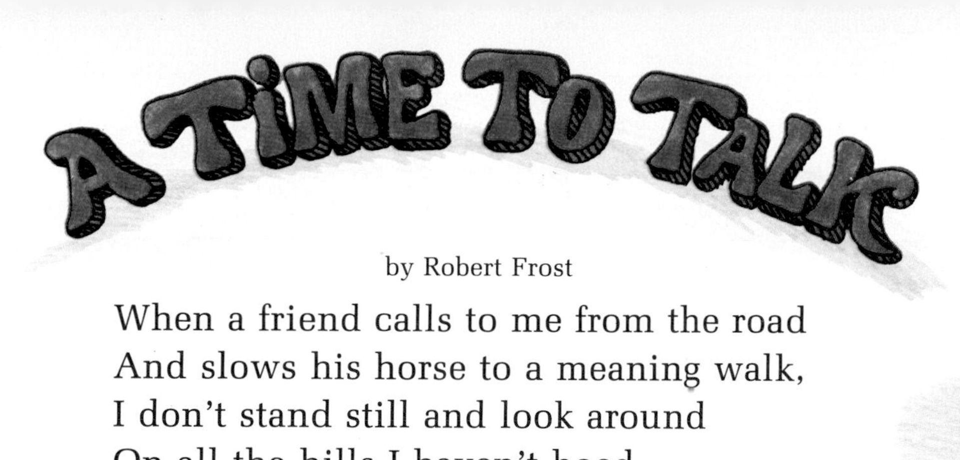

by Robert Frost

When a friend calls to me from the road
And slows his horse to a meaning walk,
I don't stand still and look around
On all the hills I haven't hoed,
And shout from where I am, "What is it?"
No, not as there is a time to talk.
I thrust my hoe in the mellow ground,
Blade-end up and five feet tall,
And plod: I go up to the stone wall
For a friendly visit.

Camel in the Sea

by LEE GARRETT GOETZ

The story, "Camel in the Sea," takes place in Somalia (so-mah'lee-uh), a small country in eastern Africa.

Mohamed (mo-hah'med) loved to go swimming in the sea. How lucky he was to live in a Somali (so-mah'lee) village right on the Indian Ocean! The sandy shore rang with the happy shouts and cries of the village boys and girls. They liked to race one another into the surf, splashing and spraying the water into a white dancing foam before they dove into the waves. Mohamed and his young sister, Asha (ie'shuh), spent all the time they could in the cool, clean sea, swimming and playing water games. They were good swimmers because their mother had taught them.

Every day except Friday, Mohamed went to school with the other village boys. The class was outdoors, and the children sat on little benches in front of the teacher in the shade of a tall palm tree. They did not have books, so the boys repeated everything the teacher said, over and over, until they knew their lessons by heart. The girls of the village did not go to school, for the people thought that school was not as important for girls as it was for boys.

On sunny days, as soon as school was over, Mohamed went with his mother and Asha to wash the family clothes. His mother stood in the water and scrubbed and pounded the clothes until they were clean. Then she handed them to Mohamed and Asha, who took them and arranged them on the beach to dry.

Mohamed had helped his mother and Asha wash the clothes ever since he could remember. He was very much surprised, therefore, one day not long before his tenth birthday, when his mother told him not to come with her and Asha.

"I do not want you to help us any more, Mohamed," his mother said. "It is time that Asha had more work to do around the house. Besides, in two more years you will be thought of as a man by our tribe, and it is not fitting that people see you always doing women's work. From now on, you help your father in the shop, and Asha will help me at home."

That first day, Mohamed felt quite grown-up and superior when he saw his mother and Asha carrying the heavy basket to the beach. But this feeling did not last long. He had no one to play with! He and Asha had played together for so long that the other children were used to his not playing with them.

Mohamed stood and watched the other boys play "kick the ball" and "hunt for the robber" and "water tag." When no one called him for a game, he turned and walked down the beach, kicking up the sand with one foot, and trying to look as though he didn't really care or want to play.

Finally, he decided to take his problem to his father, Hassan (hah'sahn).

"Mother doesn't want me to help wash the family clothes any more, Father," Mohamed told his father. "Asha has her work and her friends, but now I have no one to play with."

"Perhaps your mother is right, Mohamed," his father said, and he put down the piece of board that he held in his hand. "It is time that you should learn to help me in the shop."

Hassan was a builder of the fishing boats that went out to sea every morning and returned to the shore every evening. His small shop was right on the beach.

"When you come home from school each day, Mohamed," said his father, "I will show you the beginning of your trade. You will be a boat-builder like me."

"But Father, when will I have time for games?" Mohamed asked.

"You help me a little, and I shall see that you have plenty of time to yourself," Hassan promised. He laughed softly. "I do remember that boys need to have time to think and play. You shall have it, my son."

That summer was the driest one that anyone — even the oldest people in Mohamed's village — could recall. It did not rain at all. Each day the people would look up at the sky to see if they could see any rain clouds. But each day the sun shone brightly. There was not even one cloud to hide the sun's face for a while. Soon all the leaves of the trees started to turn brown. The flowers drooped lower and lower on their stems. Finally they became dry as paper. When the wind blew the dry leaves, they made a noise like a snake slipping through the sand.

Day after day the sun beat down, and there was no shade from the leafless trees. June and July came and went without rain. August was nearly over and still no rain.

The Old Man's Advice

Mohamed's parents and the other people of the village gathered together. Mohamed heard them ask one another, "What can we do to make it rain? Does anyone know?"

At last, they turned to the oldest man in the village for advice.

He pulled at his long white beard but did not answer. They asked him again, but he still just stroked his beard. Finally he began to speak very slowly.

"I remember when I was a small boy, there was a summer such as this. The rain was very late. The rivers dried up, and many of the fish died. The crop of corn was ruined. All the vegetables died, and the rows of bananas turned brown. Then the people asked the oldest man in our village what to do, just as you are asking me now. I will tell you what he told us. He said that when a camel could be led into the sea, then the rains would start."

When the old man had finished, all of the people started talking at once. What a clatter they made! Some said that the old man was dreaming. Others said that he was trying to play a joke on them. Finally Hassan stood up and walked over to where the old man was sitting. The people became quiet and let him speak.

"Tell us, old one, did it rain after the camel was led into the sea?"

"Unfortunately, no one was able to lead a camel into the sea," the old man replied. "The rains did not come until October. Then it was too late. We lost everything. The people left the village and never returned."

A groan went up from the crowd. Now they were not angry. They were afraid. They did not want to leave their village. Hassan spoke again.

"Even so," he said, "we must get a camel and try. Why is it hard to lead a camel into the sea, old man?"

"The camel is a beast of the desert, my son. This animal is used to taking baths in the sand. Trying to get a camel to enter water is one of the hardest things in the world to do. And to enter the sea, with the waves roaring about his knees, will frighten the most quiet of camels. Truly it is a task for a great man."

"Even if we must carry the camel on our shoulders into the sea, we must do so," Hassan said.

This made all the people laugh. They liked Hassan.

But the old man did not laugh. He shook his finger at them and said, "If you carry the camel into the sea, then you will have to carry water from the deep wells, miles away, for your crops and your animals. But if you lead him gently, then gentle rains will come down on you from above."

Silently the people got up and went to their homes. The next morning, the men hurried away to the market to buy a camel.

Mohamed went to his father's shop to await their return. In no time at all, Mohamed saw them leading a tall, cream-colored camel. Right behind the tall camel came a very clumsy little baby camel. The men had bought a mother camel and her baby.

Mohamed ran to the little camel and started running his hands over its furry body. How soft it was! A man threw him the rope that was around the baby camel's neck. "Here," he said. "Take this small one out of the way."

Mohamed led the baby camel over to his father's shop and tied the rope to a post. "Here, little one, sit down here and rest," he said. "I'll get something for you to eat."

Mohamed's mother gave him a handful of hay and some salt. She also gave him a small bag of sugar. He put all of these things in a piece of clean cloth and hurried away. The baby camel was sitting down in the shade of a boat, with all four feet tucked under its body. When Mohamed ran up, the camel turned its big, long-lashed eyes to him as if to say, "Where have you been?"

The boy opened the cloth and spread out the things his mother had given him. Then he sat down beside the baby camel and watched the men trying to get the mother camel into the sea.

How the men worked! First they tried leading her by a rope. When she came to the edge of the water, she put her feet down into the sand and refused to go any farther. Then the tallest and strongest man in the village tried to lift her back

feet up while Hassan pulled the rope. The camel sat down and refused to get up.

Then Adan Mumin (ad'uhn moo'men), a camel driver, came along. He got on her back and made her go into the shallow water. The people were excited. Maybe Adan Mumin would be successful. But when the camel saw the big waves rolling in toward her, she shook Adan Mumin off her back and ran up the beach. All of the men of the village ran after her, calling, "Stop! Stop!"

Mohamed's New Job

Mohamed and the baby camel were still sitting in the shade of one of the large fishing boats. Strange to say, when the mother camel ran up the beach, the baby camel did not try to follow her. The baby was too busy trying to open the bag of sugar Mohamed had brought.

The boy opened the bag of sugar for his new friend. "Here, little one, here is something sweet for you," he said. "Do you like sugar?"

First the little camel licked it, and then he ate a whole mouthful. Mohamed was happy. How this little camel liked sugar!

The men caught the mother camel and brought her back to the village. It was getting hot now, and they were very tired.

"Bring the baby camel here, Mohamed," said Hassan. "It must be near midday. Time to eat and sleep. We have worked hard this morning trying to get this stubborn camel into the water. Now we must rest."

Mohamed tucked the bag of sugar in his shirt and began leading the baby camel down to the beach. The little camel wanted more sugar and kept running his nose all over Mohamed's back. This tickled the boy and made him laugh.

"Please, Father," said Mohamed to Hassan. "May I take care of the little camel this afternoon? I'll be very careful not to hurt it."

Hassan smiled at his son. "If the rest of the people of our village agree, we will name you the keeper of the baby camel."

All of the people standing around agreed at once. Of course they needed someone to look after the baby camel while they were trying to lead the mother into the sea. Mohamed would be just the right one for that job.

Every morning and every afternoon Mohamed played with the baby camel on the beach. Every day he gave it some hay and salt. Every day he

gave the camel some sugar from the little bag. He also gave his camel a name. He called it "Kali" (kah'lee). In the Somali language Kali means "come here," and that was the first thing he said to the camel in the morning. Soon everyone in the village was calling the baby camel Kali.

It wasn't long before the boys of the village would come to the place where Mohamed was playing with the camel. They watched in silence for a while, and then a boy about Mohamed's age named Ibrahim (ih-brah'him) said, "I don't suppose you have much time for games, now that you have to take care of that baby camel, do you?"

"Well, of course, I must do my job," said Mohamed. "But still, I do have some time to play."

"Then come and play 'hunt for the robber' with us in the sand dunes."

Mohamed looked doubtfully at Kali. She arched her neck and stared down at the boys over her long nose. She looked so funny that they all started laughing.

Kali followed Mohamed everywhere. When he hid behind the sand dunes, she ran after him on her long, awkward legs. Of course the boys quickly found his hiding place.

Soon they were all tired, and after a quick dip in the sea, they wandered home, making plans to play the next day.

Mohamed gave Kali some extra sugar that night and rubbed her forehead gently. Kali snuggled her head under his arm and closed her eyes. After a final pat, Mohamed slipped into the house to go to bed and sleep.

The men of the village worked on the beach from morning till night, but they could not lead the mother camel into the sea. They tried other camels. Adan Mumin had a camel that was not very strong, but he could not be led into the sea. Another man had a blind camel, but as soon as he heard the roar of the waves he turned and ran away.

One day an old man led a caravan into the village. The people told him what they were trying to do and asked his help.

"My lead camel is as old as I am," he replied. "He was my pet when I was a small boy. He has followed me through the desert and across dangerous mountain passes. He will follow me anywhere, even into the sea."

The old man stood up and began blowing a little wooden whistle while he walked toward the ocean. The old camel followed him. All the people of the village were watching. The man walked out until the water was up to his neck. He was still blowing his whistle. The lead camel came to the edge of the water and then stopped. The old man blew the whistle, shouted, and waved his arms, but the camel would go no farther. The man came back to the beach and told the people, "It is impossible. No one can lead a camel into the sea."

Gently Into the Sea

One morning Mohamed got up very early. He looked out at the sea and saw that it was very calm. No wind was blowing. He put the sack of sugar in his pocket and went to get Kali. Together they went across the dusty road and down to the beach. The sun had just started to rise, but already the air was hot and breathless.

Mohamed and Kali had often played very close to the water. Each time the big waves had frightened Kali. But today the sea was very calm. Mohamed took out his little bag of sugar.

"Kali, Kali, little one, taste this sweet sugar. Come out here and I'll give you all of it."

While he was talking, Mohamed walked backwards, very slowly, into the sea. He walked carefully. He did not splash the water on himself or the baby camel.

Kali put one foot into the sea. Then she lowered her head and sniffed the water. Mohamed held out the bag of sugar. Kali stretched her neck and smelled it.

Slowly, slowly the boy and the camel walked into the sea. At last, when the water was up to her neck, Kali refused to go any farther. Mohamed didn't want to go any farther either.

He was standing on his tiptoes to keep his head out of the water. He opened the bag of sugar for Kali. The little camel put its head into the bag and ate all of the sugar.

As Kali ate, Mohamed lifted his head and saw large black clouds gathering to shut out the light of the sun.

When Mohamed looked up, he saw that all of the people of the village were on the beach watching him. They had been very quiet, because they did not want to frighten the boy or the camel. But when Mohamed and Kali came out, all the people gave a loud cheer. Hassan laid his arm across Mohamed's shoulders.

"I could not find you, my son. All of my friends started to help me look for you. Then your friend Ibrahim saw you and Kali in the sea. How proud I am of you! While we have been trying to force the big one, you have gently led the little one. I am sure that we will receive gentle rains. The wise man did not say that the camel had to be a big one. If it rains tonight, you will be the one who saved the village."

That night in the village square the people gave Kali to Mohamed to keep, and he promised to lead her into the sea whenever they needed rain. Ibrahim and all his friends laughed and clapped their hands. Then they held a feast in honor of Mohamed and the baby camel.

First everyone ate the many dishes which the women had prepared. After the remains of food had been thrown to the village dogs, the villagers brought out the big drums. Dancers began dancing to the music of the drums.

They had not been dancing very long when a few drops of rain fell on the dry earth. The people looked up and laughed with delight.

Dark clouds had gathered and hid the light of the moon. More rain came. It was a gentle rain, but it did not stop. The thirsty earth drank the raindrops. The people called to each other that now the crops would not die, that the flowers would start to blossom again, and that they would not have to leave the village that they loved.

Mohamed left his playmates and took Kali into the house as soon as it started to rain. He snuggled down against her warm coat and listened to the villagers talking. Mohamed listened to the sound of the rain as it fell on the thatched roofs and dripped onto the ground.

"Indeed it was a good day for our village when you came, Kali," he whispered into Kali's ear. Soon the warmth of Kali and the lateness of the night made him fall asleep.

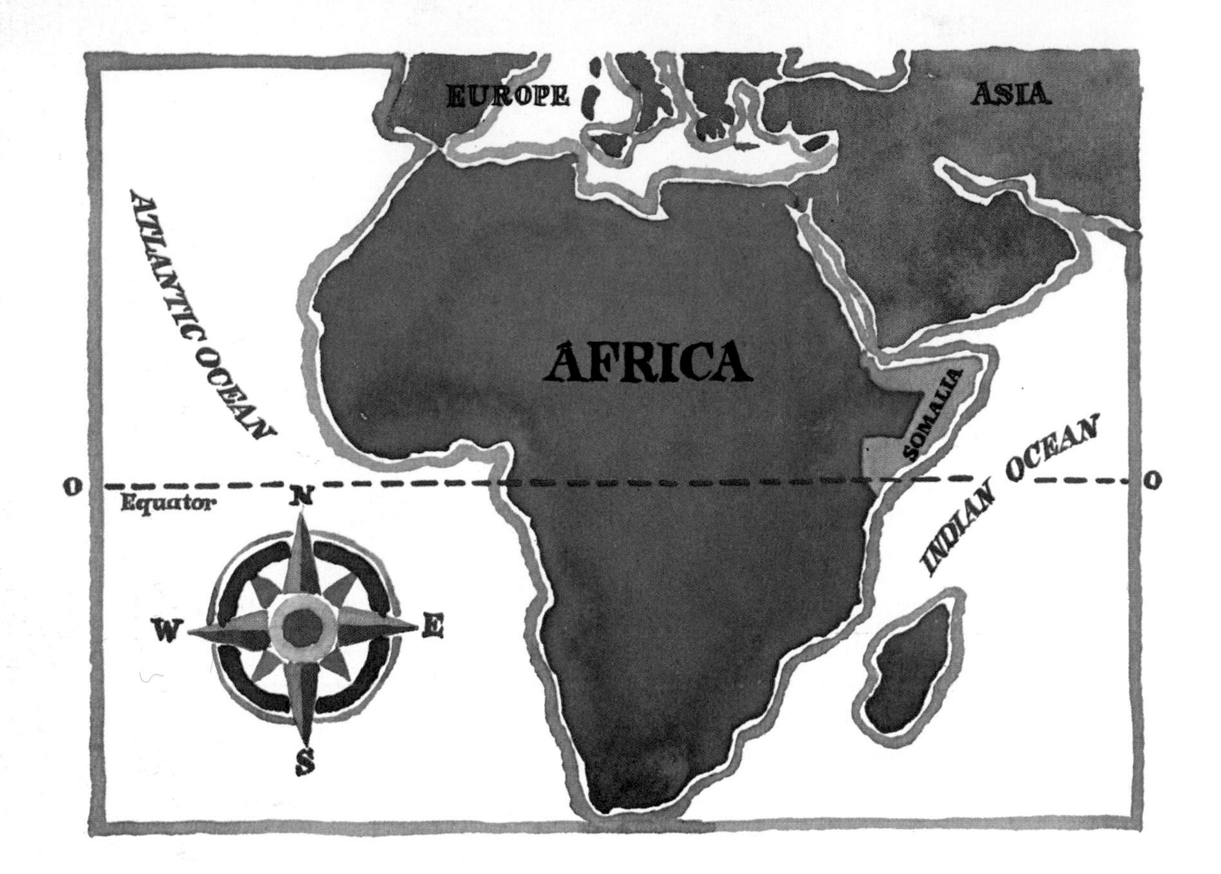

AUTHOR

Lee Garrett Goetz is very familiar with the country in which this story takes place, for she has lived in Somalia for several years. Her husband is the director of a United States government English-language program there. Mr. and Mrs. Goetz and their two sons live in a house that overlooks the Indian Ocean.

Mrs. Goetz was born in Columbus, Ohio, but has lived in almost every state and in several other countries. She is now teaching in the English Language Center in Somalia. She has also written a book, to be used at this Center, about the lives of famous Americans.

THE CAMEL

The camel has a single hump;
The dromedary, two;
Or else the other way around.
I'm never sure. Are you?

– *Ogden Nash*

THE DUCK

Behold the duck.
It does not cluck.
A cluck it lacks.
It quacks.
It is specially fond
Of a puddle or pond.
When it dines or sups,
It bottoms ups.

– *Ogden Nash*

VISITORS

In winter when people pay a call
On us, they hurry inside our hall
And quickly shut the outside door
And slap their hands and stamp the floor,
And then they talk about the snow
For hours, until it's time to go.

Then, all wrapped up in their mufflers, they
Remember what they had meant to say.
They stand there in the open door
And start to remember more and more
While Mummy smiles and smiles, and freezes,
Til Daddy deliberately sneezes.

— *Harry Behn*

BRAVE KATE SHELLEY

by Louis Wolfe

The name Kate Shelley is well known in American railroad history. No woman ever showed more courage than this fifteen-year-old girl in her struggle to save a trainload of passengers from death.

Kate was the oldest of five children. Her family lived in a farm village in Iowa. Her mother ran the house, raised five children, and did much of the farming. Her father worked as a section foreman on the Chicago and North Western Railway.

The Shelley family house stood on a slope overlooking Honey Creek, a small brook that flowed into the Des Moines (duh-moin′) River.

Kate often looked out the window and watched the trains roll over Honey Creek bridge. Her eyes danced whenever she saw her father walking home from work beside the tracks.

In 1878, great misfortune struck the Shelley home. Kate's father was killed in a railroad accident. A short while later her brother was drowned. From then on, Kate had to take on many of the household chores to help her overworked mother. She helped care for the children, plow the fields, harvest the crops, and feed the livestock. Besides all that, she went to school.

On the morning of July 6, 1881, the air was hot and sticky. Not a breeze stirred. As Kate hoed away in the cornfield, she glanced at the sky. "Dark clouds gathering over there," she mumbled. "Guess we'll have a storm."

By mid-afternoon the swift-moving clouds blotted out the sun. Thunder rumbled in the distance, and a strong wind began to blow.

Later, as Kate served supper to the children, the sky grew darker and the thunder came closer and closer. Suddenly there was a jagged flash of lightning and a crash of thunder. The rain came down in torrents and streamed down into Honey Creek.

Kate put the frightened children to bed. Then she and her mother sat by the window. Neither spoke. In the blinding brightness of the lightning, they saw the rain come down in sheets. They saw streams of water rushing up against the barn halfway down the slope. They saw the creek rising faster and faster.

Kate now feared for the livestock in the barn. The rushing water would soon sweep the barn into the creek. The trapped animals would not have a chance.

Kate threw a jacket over her shoulders.

"Mother," she said, "I'm going to let the livestock out of the barn." Sloshing through water and mud a foot deep, Kate made her way down the slope and opened the barn door. The panicky cows, horses, and pigs plunged outside and dashed wildly up the slope to higher ground.

Back in the house, Kate changed her clothes and sat down again with her mother near the window. It was now eleven o'clock. Honey Creek was rising. With each flash of lightning, Kate saw the brook climb higher and closer to the railroad bridge. Would that weak wooden bridge hold?

Just then Kate heard something. It was the rumble of an engine crossing the Des Moines River bridge about a mile away. A short time

later she saw a weak headlight stabbing through the dark. The engine had been sent out to check track conditions.

In a flash of lightning, Kate saw the engine chug toward the battered Honey Creek bridge. Pressing her face against the windowpane, she breathed faster as the engine rolled onto the bridge. The bell rang once . . . twice . . . . Then there was an earsplitting crash of the bridge giving way, a thundering splash, and the hissing of steam.

"Mother! Mother!" Kate screamed. "The bridge caved in! The engine fell into the creek!"

Then Kate and her mother sat in terrified silence. They peered out into the inky blackness and waited. Now the only sounds came from the steady downpour, the roll of distant thunder, and the rapid flow of water through the creek. In her mind, Kate could see the engine and its crew buried in the muddy water.

Suddenly a more horrifying thought flashed through her mind. The midnight express! It was due soon! It was packed with passengers!

Without hesitating a second, Kate tied a hat on her head, threw on a jacket, and grabbed a lantern.

"Kate!" her mother cried. "Where are you going?"

The girl jerked open the door. "I'm going to Mongoina station. I'll tell them the Honey Creek bridge is down so they can flag the midnight express to stop."

"Don't go, Kate!" Mrs. Shelley begged. "Don't!" But the girl was already out and on her way.

Lantern in hand, she pushed on against the storm and finally reached the approach to the bridge. She looked down into the creek. Nothing. She waved her lantern. Nothing. She waved it again and again. Above the roar of the swelling water, she thought she heard faint voices calling. But there was nothing she could do, and time was running short. So she put her hand to her mouth and called down, "I'll be back with help as soon as I can."

Struggle on the Bridge

Leaning forward and holding her head low, Kate groped ahead. Mongoina station was only a mile down the tracks. But in such a storm it was a mighty long mile. She still had to cross the long wooden bridge that went over the Des Moines River. She must hurry.

When she reached the eastern end of the bridge, she stopped short. The river was swollen higher than ever before. Now and then the bridge groaned and creaked as if it too might give way.

Kate knew this bridge well. It had been built purposely with the ties far apart to discourage people from crossing it. The only path for track walkers was a narrow board, and much of that had rotted away. To cross the bridge in broad daylight was dangerous. To cross it at night in such a storm was almost impossible.

Kate drew back a step. No, she must not risk it. But then she thought of the midnight express . . . the hundreds of men and women and children passengers. Kate clenched her teeth, gripped her lantern tighter, and started across.

With her very first step, her foot slipped on a mud-covered tie. She fell forward, one foot and one arm sticking downward through the ties.

The thundering torrent below put out the lantern, pulled at her arm and leg, and almost sucked her in. But Kate struggled frantically and managed to push herself up in time.

Soaked to the skin and gasping for breath, the girl realized then that she could never walk across that bridge. She would have to crawl across on her hands and knees. Using one hand to grip the rail and the other to reach forward from tie to tie, Kate crawled as fast as she dared.

Carefully, very carefully, she groped her way through the rain and darkness. Splinters ripped her dress. Slippery ties made her lose her grip.

Pieces of driftwood stuck up from the river and battered her arms and legs. Rusty nails gashed her hands and knees. Once a strong gust of wind swept a wave over her, and Kate had to lie face downward and clutch the rails to keep from being washed into the river.

After what seemed to be hours, Kate reached out and struck dirt. She crawled ahead, reached out, and struck dirt again. At last! She had crossed the bridge!

Although every muscle in her body ached and she could barely move, Kate struggled to her feet. Then she staggered up the tracks and stumbled into Mongoina station — only a few minutes before midnight. With her last few breaths she gasped out her warning, and then fainted.

Someone said, "The girl is crazy!" But the stationmaster knew Kate and didn't waste a second. He grabbed a red lantern, dashed out onto the tracks, and waved it wildly.

And just in time! About a mile down the tracks, the midnight express came pounding at full speed. Suddenly there was a screeching of brakes. Sparks flew from the engine's giant wheels, and the train ground to a stop right in front of the station.

The engineer jumped from the train and stormed over to the stationmaster. "What's the idea?" he exploded.

The angry conductor shouted, "Of all places to stop an express train!"

Of course, when the stationmaster explained about Kate and the Honey Creek Bridge, the engineer and conductor quickly calmed down. Many of the passengers, who had also piled out of the train, sighed with relief and thankfulness. Inside the station they gathered around Kate, who by now had come to. The men thanked the young girl for saving their lives. Tears streaming from their eyes, the women passengers hugged and kissed the girl.

But the moment Kate's mind was clear again, she thought of the men trapped in Honey Creek. She begged that a rescue party be sent there at once. She offered to go along and guide them to the spot.

A short while later, an engine, loaded with shovels, ropes, and other rescue gear, was pounding down the tracks toward Honey Creek. Kate and the rescue party arrived in time to save the brakeman and engineer.

For the next few days, the news of Kate Shelley's act of courage spread all over the country. Today railroad men still tell the story of this young girl's brave deed.

AUTHOR

Louis Wolfe was born in New Jersey, and he and his wife now live in New York City. For many years he was a teacher in the New York public schools. He has also worked as an announcer and storyteller, speaking on radio programs and at camps and recreation centers.

The story, "Brave Kate Shelley," appears in Mr. Wolfe's book, *Clear the Track.* Mr. Wolfe has also written *Let's Go to a Weather Station, Let's Go to a Planetarium, Let's Go to City Hall, Let's Go to the Klondike Gold Rush,* and *Ifrikiya: Stories About Africa and Africans.*

Skill Lesson 5:

MAKING MENTAL PICTURES

In at least one way, a person who writes a story is like an artist who paints pictures. Each of them tries to make pictures for us. An artist uses paints to make real pictures. A person who writes a story uses words to help us make pictures in our minds.

There are real pictures in almost any story you will read. But those pictures do not show everything that the words tell about. To understand and enjoy a story as much as you can, you will need to imagine what things in the story would look like if you really saw them. Doing this can be called **making mental pictures.**

The words in a story will tell you much that you can use to help you make such mental pictures. Any picture you imagine of a person, thing, or happening in a story should fit well with what the words say. It should not have in it anything that does not agree with those words.

As you read the following paragraph, imagine a picture of the cowboy who is being talked about:

> The first real cowboy Billy ever saw didn't look the way he thought a cowboy would look. He was tall, but he was standing beside a jeep instead of sitting on a horse. He was wearing blue pants that looked like those Billy wore to school. He had on a red shirt that was open at the neck. He wasn't wearing a hat, and he didn't have guns or a rope. Billy was glad to see, though, that he was wearing brown cowboy boots. That made him seem more like a cowboy.

Could you make a picture in your mind of the cowboy that Billy saw?

Here are pictures of four cowboys. Which picture is most like the one you made in your mind?

Discussion

Help your class answer these questions:

1. How are an artist and a person who writes a story alike?
2. How can making pictures in your mind help you as you read a story?
3. What should be true about pictures you imagine as you read a story?
4. What can you do to help you imagine pictures that are good ones?
5. Which picture shows the cowboy that Billy saw? How did you know that each of the others was wrong?

On your own

As you read the following, imagine pictures that would fit the things that are happening.

Bob was trying to fix the chain on his new red bicycle. He had it turned upside down on the grass as he worked. A big brown dog walked up to him and said, "You'll have to take the back wheel off before you can fix the chain."

Bob was so surprised that he didn't know what to do. Just then the man who owned the dog came up. When Bob told him what the dog had said, the man said, "Don't listen to him. He doesn't know how to fix a bicycle."

Checking your work

Which of the following rows of pictures is most like the pictures that you made in your mind? Tell your class why you picked the pictures that you did.

WIND SONG

When the wind blows
The quiet things speak.
Some whisper, some clang,
Some creak.

Grasses swish.
Treetops sigh.
Flags slap
and snap at the sky.
Wires on poles
whistle and hum.
Ashcans roll.
Windows drum.

When the wind goes —
suddenly
then,
the quiet things
are quiet again.

– Lilian Moore

COMMANDS

by Harriet Carlson

In the past:
Pump some water.
Hitch the horses.
Don't waste candles.
Bar the door.
Kindle the fire.
Milk the cow now.

Today:
Turn out the lights.
Run to the store.
Wash the car.
Turn down TV.
Walk the dog.
Get off the phone.

In the future:
Fuel the rocket.
Start the learning machine.
Get off the television phone.
Clean the computer.
Desalt some ocean water.
Don't go to Mars before supper.

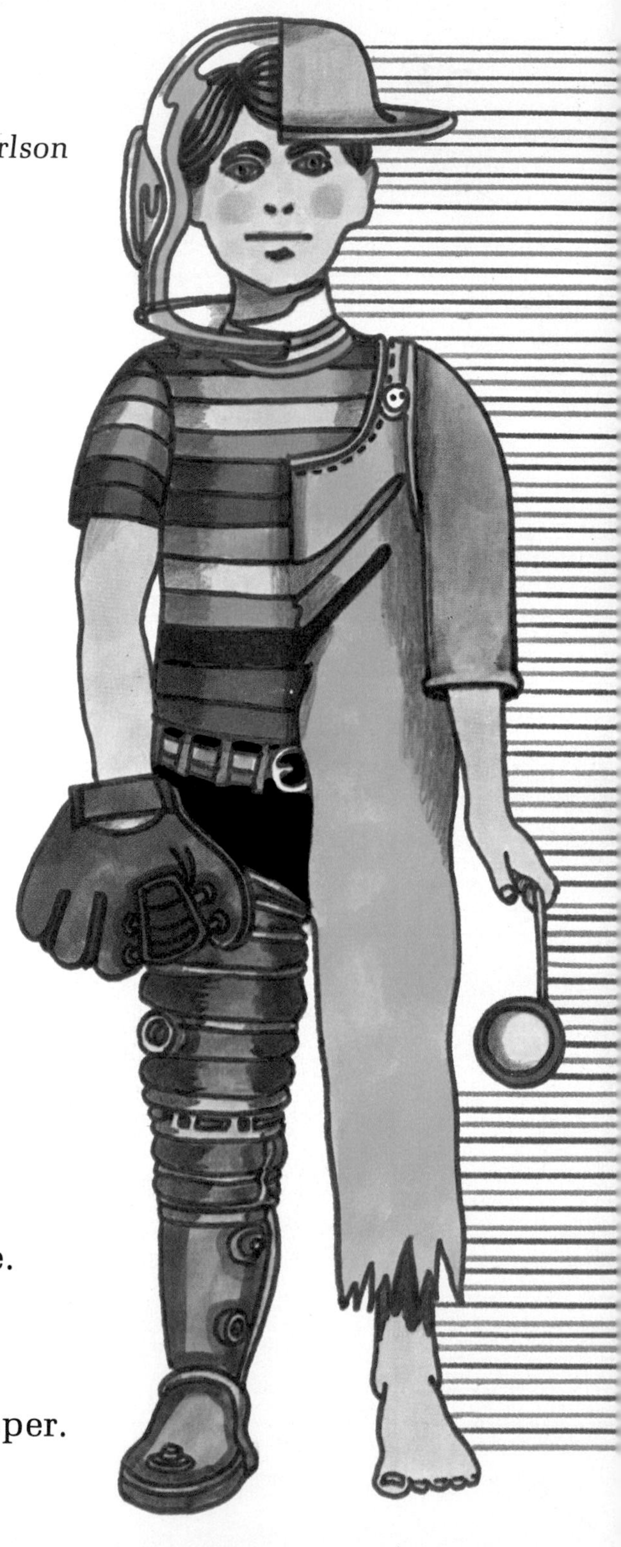

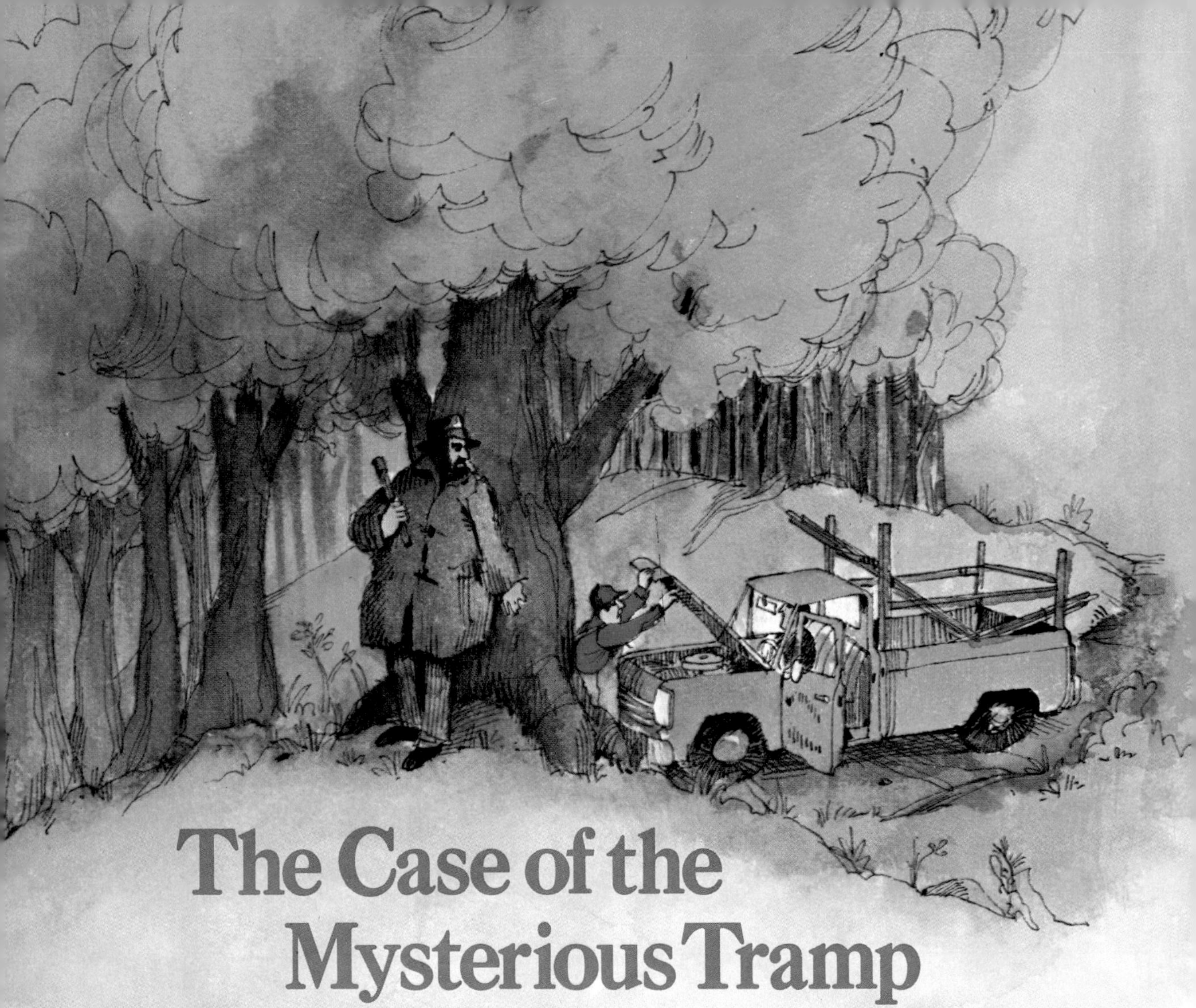

The Case of the Mysterious Tramp

by Donald J. Sobol

His head bent low over the handlebars of his bike, Encyclopedia Brown rounded the corner of Beech Street like high-speed sandpaper.

It was three minutes before six o'clock of a summer evening. With a bit of luck and a following wind,

Encyclopedia hoped to make it home on time for dinner.

Suddenly someone called his name.

"Leroy! Leroy Brown!"

Right off he knew it had to be a teacher calling. Only teachers and his mother and father called him Leroy.

Everyone else in the town of Idaville called him Encyclopedia.

He didn't look much like an encyclopedia, which is a set of books filled with all kinds of facts. People called him Encyclopedia because he had read more books than a bathtub full of professors. And he never forgot anything he read.

"Leroy! Leroy!"

It was Mrs. Worth, his old second-grade teacher. She was standing beside her car, looking very sad.

"I can't get it going," she said. "Can you help me?"

"I'll try," said Encyclopedia. He leaned his bike against a tree and raised the hood of the car.

"Start her again, please, Mrs. Worth," he said.

The motor coughed and sputtered out.

"The trouble must be in the carburetor," said Encyclopedia, beginning to disappear under the hood.

He lifted off the air filter. Now he could reach the butterfly valve in the carburetor. He poked it open with his finger.

The motor roared to life when Mrs. Worth again tried to start it.

Mrs. Worth was delighted. When Encyclopedia returned to view, she thanked him over and over again.

"Oh, it wasn't anything," said Encyclopedia. "Just a stuck valve."

He smiled as Mrs. Worth drove off — till he looked at his watch. It gave him unsmiling news. It was past six o'clock, the Browns' dinner hour. He'd catch it for being late!

His mother put down a pot of boiled cabbage to stare at him. Dirt and grease from Mrs. Worth's motor coated him from ears to sneakers.

"Where have you been?" she asked, kissing the one clean spot on his cheek.

"Riding my bike," answered Encyclopedia.

He didn't mention Mrs. Worth's motor. He hardly ever spoke to anyone, not even his parents, about the help he gave others. And he *never* spoke about the help he gave grown-ups.

His mother looked out at Rover Avenue through the kitchen window. Strangely enough, she hadn't scolded him for being late.

"Your father knows we are having corned beef and cabbage tonight," she said in a worried voice. "What could be keeping him?"

"Dad wouldn't miss his favorite dish without a good reason," said Encyclopedia. "Maybe he's chasing a dangerous crook or something."

Mrs. Brown looked even more worried.

Encyclopedia tried again. "Don't worry, Mom," he said. "Dad is the best police officer in the state. He'll be home soon."

Encyclopedia was right. As he was washing the back of his neck, he heard his father close the garage door.

A moment later, Mr. Brown entered the house. He was a big, broad-shouldered man dressed in a police chief's uniform.

His uniform was the envy of every lawman in the United States. Although Idaville was like many other American towns, its police force was *unlike* any other.

For more than a year, neither child nor grown-up had gotten away with breaking a law.

Hardened criminals had passed the word: "Stay clear of Idaville."

This was partly because the Idaville policemen were well trained, smart, and brave. But mostly it was because Chief Brown had Encyclopedia at the dinner table.

Chief Brown never whispered a word of how Encyclopedia helped him. After all, who would believe the truth?

Who would believe that a young boy solved difficult cases while eating dinner in the Browns' red brick house on Rover Avenue?

Naturally, Encyclopedia never let out that he was the mastermind behind Idaville's war on crime. So the name Leroy Brown was missing from the honor roll of the world's great detectives.

"I'm sorry to be late, dear," said Chief Brown as he sat down to eat. "A terrible thing happened this afternoon. Mr. Clancy, the plumber, was beaten and robbed."

"Was he badly hurt?" asked Mrs. Brown.

"He's in the city hospital," Chief Brown said.

"The doctors say he'll be all right. I'm afraid we'll never catch the man who attacked him."

"Why not, Dad?" asked Encyclopedia. "Didn't anyone see what happened?"

"John Morgan saw everything," said Chief Brown. "He's Mr. Clancy's helper. He was sitting in the truck when a tramp attacked Mr. Clancy."

Chief Brown unbuttoned his breast pocket and drew out his notebook. "I wrote down everything John Morgan told me. I'll read it to you."

Encyclopedia closed his eyes. He always closed his eyes when he did his heavy thinking on a case.

His father began to read what John Morgan had told him about the beating and theft:

"Clancy was driving the truck, and I was sitting beside him. We had turned onto the dirt road near the Benson farm when the motor overheated. Clancy stopped, walked around to the front of the truck, and

lifted the hood. As he took off the radiator cap, a tramp jumped out of the woods. The tramp struck Clancy on the head with a piece of pipe.

"Clancy fell over the radiator and slid down the front of the truck. I leaped out of the truck, but the tramp was already racing into the woods. He carried the pipe and Clancy's billfold. I let him go in order to get Clancy to the hospital right away."

Chief Brown finished reading and closed his notebook.

Encyclopedia opened his eyes. He asked but one question: "Did Mr. Clancy have an unusually large amount of money in his billfold?"

His father looked startled.

"Why, yes," he answered. "It so happened that Mr. Clancy had two hundred dollars in his billfold. He had just been paid for work on a new apartment house. What made you think he was carrying a lot of money?"

"He had to be," said Encyclopedia. "Now you should have no trouble finding the man who struck and robbed him."

"No trouble?" said Chief Brown. "The woods come out on the railroad tracks. It's a sure bet that the tramp hopped a ride on a freight train. He's probably in another state by now."

GTAX

"You'll find him where John Morgan lives — and the two hundred dollars besides," said Encyclopedia.

"Do you think John Morgan helped the tramp rob Mr. Clancy?" asked Mrs. Brown.

"No," answered Encyclopedia.

"Well, what do you think?" asked Chief Brown.

"I think that when Mr. Clancy stopped the truck in the woods, John Morgan saw his chance," answered Encyclopedia. "While Mr. Clancy was checking the radiator, John Morgan sneaked from the truck,

knocked him out, and stole his billfold with the two hundred dollars."

"What about the tramp?" asked Chief Brown.

"There never was a tramp, Dad," said Encyclopedia. "John Morgan made him up. John Morgan robbed Mr. Clancy by himself and then drove him to the hospital."

Chief Brown rubbed his chin thoughtfully. "That could be what really happened," he said. "But I can't prove it."

"The proof is down in black and white," said Encyclopedia. "Just read over what John Morgan told you. He gives himself away!"

HOW DID JOHN MORGAN GIVE HIMSELF AWAY?

(Turn the page for the solution to "The Case of the Mysterious Tramp.")

AUTHOR

Born in New York City, Donald J. Sobol first worked for a newspaper and then for a department store. He then decided to become a writer. He has been glad of it ever since, because his books have been very popular. He also writes stories and articles for newspapers and magazines.

Mr. Sobol and his wife and four children live in Florida. The Sobols own two cars — both made in the year 1930!

Old cars are not only Mr. Sobol's hobby, but they are put to good use. He drives one of them every weekday, and he says that the other one is his "Sunday car."

The story you just read is from *Encyclopedia Brown Finds the Clues.* Other books about this young hero are:

Encyclopedia Brown and the Case of the Secret Pitch
Encyclopedia Brown, Boy Detective
Encyclopedia Brown Gets His Man
Encyclopedia Brown Keeps the Peace
Encyclopedia Brown Solves Them All

Solution to "The Case of the Mysterious Tramp"

John Morgan said that Mr. Clancy walked around to the front of the truck and raised the hood.

He described how "Clancy fell over the radiator and slid down the front of the truck" after being struck by the tramp. Then he himself "climbed out of the truck."

But he said he had been sitting in the front seat. So he saw the attack through the windshield.

Impossible!

The hood of the truck was raised, remember?

All John Morgan could have seen through the windshield was the hood!

Chief Brown recovered Mr. Clancy's money. The guilty John Morgan was sent to jail.

To be answered in our next issue

When a great tree falls
And people aren't near,
Does it make a noise
If no one can hear?
And which came first,
The hen or the egg?
This impractical question
We ask and then beg.
Some wise men say
It's beyond their ken.
Did anyone ever
Ask the hen?

— AUTHOR UNKNOWN

Funny things always seem to happen to Rupert. In this chapter from The Terrible Troubles of Rupert Piper, *Rupert tells about the evening his mother asked him to do a "kind, terrible deed."*

Rupert Piper Becomes A Hero

by Ethelyn Parkinson

It all began the morning that Miss Carlman said, "Boys and girls, we have to get some new pictures for the school hall. The ones out there are old and faded and yellow. Does anyone in the class have a good idea?"

Milt waved. "Miss Carlman, I read a very educational article."

"We-ell!" Miss Carlman said.

Milt nodded. "This article was on decorating rooms, and it said pictures should be chosen with great care. There's a baseball pitcher who's a very great hero, so if the fellows have the say . . ."

"The boys," Miss Carlman stated, "will not have *all* the say."

Sylvia waved. "Miss Carlman, Leonard Posey

received a beautiful flash camera for his birthday. Maybe he could take classroom pictures and take some outside of school, too. They would look lovely in the hall."

"An interesting idea," Miss Carlman said. "Leonard is absent with a cold, but I'll talk to him. Ready for recess!"

The fellows went down to the **NO DAMES** corner to talk things over.

"A fine thing!" said Trowbridge (Doodleberries) Hall. "A fine thing having Nosey Posey getting pictures of us. No telling what kind of pictures he'll take!"

Dood was right. Saturday evening I was having a little after-dinner lunch on the sofa when Annabelle's mother came to see my Mom about some club meeting. She brought her sewing.

"I'm making a dress for Annabelle," she said. She held it up. It was made of some pink stuff. "It's a surprise. I'd like to finish it this evening."

So Mom got her sewing, and they talked and sewed.

"I'm ready to turn this hem," Mrs. Willman said. "I wonder just how much to turn up. It's quite a problem without Annabelle — or someone who's just her height."

They looked at me. I could feel some little cold goose bumps getting stirred up on my backbone.

"I wonder . . ." Mom said. "Rupert, dear." Mom used her special voice that means I am going to have to do some kind, terrible deed.

I stuffed my cupcake in my mouth and dived for the door, but Mom grabbed me.

"Rupert, dear," she said, "just slip this pretty dress on for a minute. I know you'd love to do Annabelle's mother a little favor."

I'd rather be dead three times.

"I feel very sick," I said. "I itch all over. Mom, you wouldn't want me to break out with measles in Annabelle's dress."

"Stand still, Rupert," Mom said.

Then they did it. Mom got a wrestler's hold on me, and Mrs. Willman pulled Annabelle's old dress over my head.

I was never so disgraced. But the worst was yet to come.

The doorbell rang. Mom went to answer, and I heard a terrible voice saying, "Is Rupert busy?"

In walked Nosey Posey with his camera. He smiled at me very sweetly. "Good evening," he said. "You're looking charming this evening."

I showed him my teeth so Mom would think I was smiling. "Who invited you?" I said.

"*Rupert!*" said Mom.

"I was passing by," Leonard said, "and I saw you standing there looking lovely, so I came in to compliment you." He was monkeying with his camera.

Mom brought some pins for Mrs. Willman. "Stand still, Rupert," Mom said.

Right then the camera flashed in my eyes.

Leonard smiled at me. "Well, good-by, Beautiful," he said. "I'll see you in my dreams." He hurried out.

I knew what he was going to do. He was going to take the film to the drugstore, and he was going to have pictures of me in Annabelle's dress to show around, and I *was* going to die three times.

"Gangway!" I yelled. "I'm going!"

"Rupert!" Mom dived for me, but I got through the door.

I jumped off the porch and ran after Nosey. He heard me coming and ducked into Peck's Grocery drive. I ran down the other side and scrambled over the hedge and gained on him.

He dashed out into Gray Street and began to yell, "Help! Help! Murder!"

Mrs. Haverkorn was talking to Mrs. Pipgrass. "Why, see that girl chasing Leonard Posey!" Mrs. Haverkorn said. "My goodness, isn't that disgraceful?"

Leonard ran down Hubbard and dashed across Oak Street and ran toward the river howling for help. Then he disappeared.

I thought fast. There was just one place to disappear. Leonard had climbed down the ladder into Mr. Peterson's boat that's always tied to the dock.

Only tonight it wasn't there. I ran and peeked over. Sure enough, there was Nosey standing on the ladder below me. He was just one foot above the water, which was very shallow, but wet.

"Okay, chum. Hand up that camera," I said.

"It's mine!" he yelled.

"Okay," I said. I sat down on the dock. "I hope you are very comfortable down there, pal, as you are going to stay there all night."

"Rupert Piper," Leonard howled. "You let me come up!"

"Nobody's stopping you," I said, with a very sweet smile. "Come on! I'll give you a hand."

"I'll tell my mother on you!" he yelled. "I'll tell Miss Carlman!"

"Come on up," I said, "and tell them."

He began to howl, "Help!" And who should come down but Police Chief Fox!

"What's going on here?" he said.

"Piper won't let me come up!" Leonard yelled.

Chief Fox laughed. "So it's you, Rupert! I thought some girl had chased some boy down there."

"I was doing a kind deed," I said, "when he walked into our house and took a picture of me. All I want is the film."

"This film belongs to my sister!" Leonard yelled.

"Rupert, hold my billy club," Chief Fox said. He reached in his pocket. There was a flash.

I turned around. "Hey!" I said. "Are you taking pictures, too?"

"Come on up, Leonard," Chief Fox said. "We'll go over to Hanen's Drugstore and have our films developed. Put your dress in my car and come along, Rupert. I got a good shot of you."

Behind a fellow's back! And I thought Chief Fox was my friend! My heart broke.

We went to the drugstore, and Mr. Hanen developed the films and printed them right away. Leonard laughed very loud at his picture of me. "Boy, that will sure look cute in the hall at Lincoln School!"

"Mine, too," said Chief Fox. "Got a fine shot of you, Leonard — chased right into the river — by a girl!"

"A *girl*?" Leonard squeaked. "Chief Fox, you know that's Rupert!"

"Looks like a girl to me!" Chief Fox said. He showed us the picture. There was Leonard, hanging onto the ladder looking scared. On

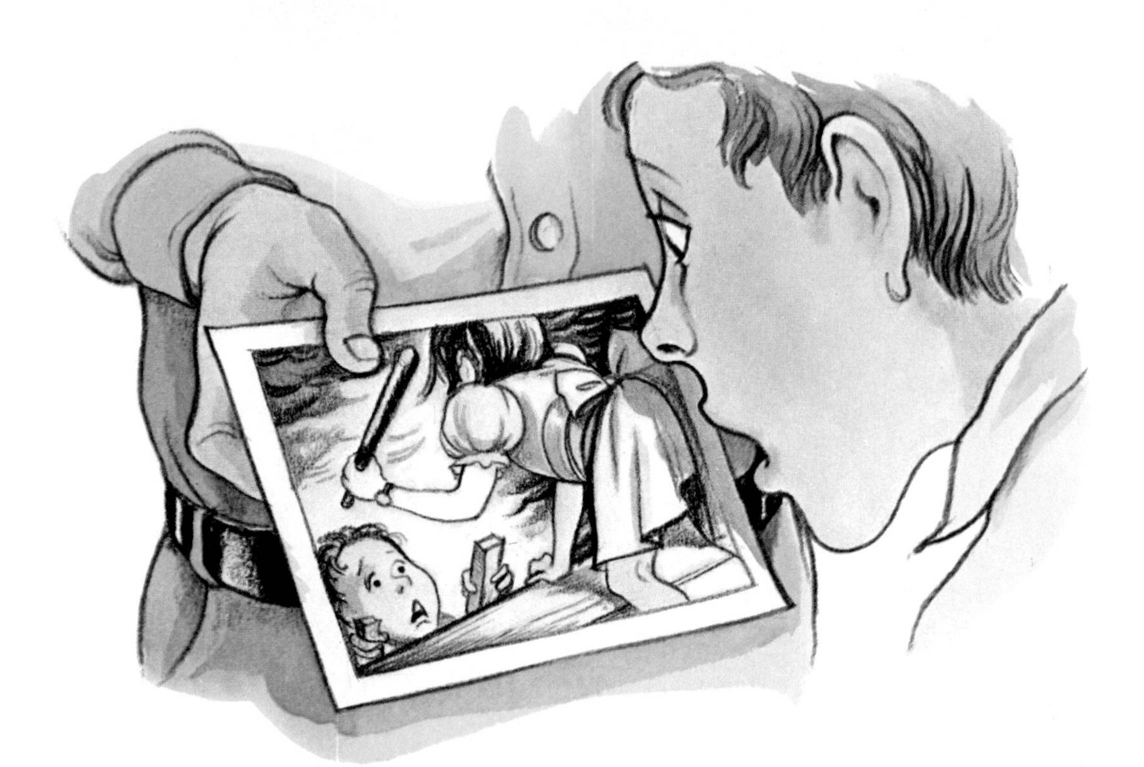

the dock was a girl with a club. That's how it looked.

"Pretty cute!" Chief Fox bragged. "I'd like about thirty prints. How many are you ordering, Leonard?"

Leonard looked kind of sick. "Well, it's really Rupert's picture," he said, "so I guess I'll just give it to him."

Chief Fox said, "Suppose you do that right now."

So Leonard gave me the film and the print, and I tore them up.

"I changed my mind," Chief Fox said. "I won't have any pictures made — unless you really need some, Rupert." He winked at me.

"No, I won't need any," I said.

"That sounds like a bargain, gentlemen," Chief Fox said. "And now how about a soda?"

When I got home, Mom and Annabelle's mother were waiting.

"Rupert," Mom said. "Where is Annabelle's dress?" Mom looked really worried.

"It's right here," I said. "Mr. Hanen gave me this bag."

I told them all about it. "I had to settle things with Leonard because this is Annabelle's dress. My face didn't show in Chief Fox's picture, and people would think it was Annabelle who had chased Leonard down the ladder and was standing over him with a club, and Annabelle would be disgraced!"

There was a scratch on my arm from Mrs. Haverkorn's hedge. I held my arm up and rubbed it.

"You poor boy!" Mrs. Willman said. "Getting wounded — for Annabelle! You're really a hero!" She winked at Mom.

"Well, in that case," Mom said, "there's one piece of cake left — hero!"

Leonard did take some keen pictures of our class and the other classes in the school. Miss Carlman put them up in the hall, and they looked very keen.

But I shook a little when I thought what *might* have happened to me! Thanksgiving was just around the corner, and I had something to be thankful for.

AUTHOR

You might enjoy reading the rest of *The Terrible Troubles of Rupert Piper* by Ethelyn Parkinson.

There is also another book about Rupert, *The Operation That Happened to Rupert Piper.* The story idea for this might well have come from the days when Ethelyn Parkinson was studying to be a nurse. She later decided to become a writer instead, but she says that she has many happy memories of her nursing education.

Ethelyn Parkinson was born in Green Bay, Wisconsin, where she still lives. Miss Parkinson says that most of her story ideas come from being around her nephews and nieces and from her own happy childhood. Some of her other books for boys and girls are *Good Old Archibald, The Merry Mad Bachelors, Elf King Joe,* and *Today I Am a Ham.*

Skill Lesson 6:

RECOGNIZING THE POWER OF WORDS

Words are really wonderful things. Sometimes they help us to paint a picture in our minds, and they can also make us feel happy or sad. A person who writes a story or a poem chooses words that help us to understand his feelings about places, people, or things.

Each numbered sentence below is what someone might write to describe a fog that was closing in around him. Can you see any difference in the words which have been chosen to describe the fog?

1. I could see less and less as a thick fog came up around me.
2. Slowly, slowly, the fog rolled nearer and nearer, until it brushed my cheeks and erased all the trees and earth around me.

3. The fog crept in as silently as a shadow, spreading its web-like curtain on the walls of the sky, and I was caught in its silk cocoon.

What word is used in Sentence 1 to describe the fog?

Sentence 2 uses words that tell how slowly the fog comes near to the person, and how close and really thick it is.

Sentence 3 uses very different words to describe the coming of the fog. Notice that, unlike the other two sentences, it gives some idea as to how the person felt. Can you find the metaphors and similes in Sentences 2 and 3?

An author uses words in different ways to get you to feel something about what he is saying. We call these words **descriptive words.** Descriptive words are something like words that help you to paint a picture in your mind. But many times descriptive words help you to do more than just *see* such a picture. They can help you *feel,* or even *smell, taste,* or *hear* what the author is talking about.

Discussion

Help your class answer these questions:

1. What words in Sentence 1 describe the fog and tell you where it is?

2. What words in Sentence 2 does the author use to tell you that the fog is very, very close to the person?
3. When the author says, in Sentence 2, that the fog "erased all the trees and earth around me," what does that mean to you? What happens when you erase something? Were the trees and earth *really* erased? How are the words *brushed* and *erased* both metaphors?
4. What do the words "crept in as silently as a shadow" tell you about the fog? What is the simile in those words? What other simile is there in Sentence 3?
5. In Sentence 3, what is the fog being compared to by the metaphor, "was spreading its web-like curtain on the walls of the sky"?
6. Why is "I was caught in its silk cocoon" a metaphor?

On your own

As you read the following two paragraphs to yourself, notice the words that are used to describe how the puppy *felt*. What do the other words help you to see or hear?

The puppy was very sad. He sat alone on the steps. He didn't have anyone to play with.

Then two boys came along. The puppy chased

them. They made a lot of noise. They all fell down in a heap.

Now read the next two paragraphs about the same puppy, and try to decide why the two stories about the same thing are really quite different. As you read, notice the words that are used to make you feel happy or sad or lonely, and those that help you see and hear what was happening.

It was an unhappy picture. The poor little puppy sat all alone at the foot of the steps . . . as if he didn't have a friend in the whole wide world. His sad brown eyes seemed to be pleading for someone to come to talk or to play with him. One ear drooped like a wet dishrag, and he slumped his body down as if his legs could never lift his load of sadness. The only sound to be heard was the steady buzz of a fly that circled the puppy's head. The dog didn't move or blink an eye. He just sat —a lonely lump of sadness.

Suddenly, around the corner of the house two boys came flying, one behind the other. The "wet dishrag" perked up, the eyes shone, the limp legs stiffened and pushed the body into motion, and the puppy took off in wild chase. The noise was deafening. The air was filled with shouts, and barks, and laughter, all tangled in a pile of arms and legs and a thumping, wagging puppy tail.

Checking your work

If you are asked to do so, compare the feelings you had as you read the second pair of paragraphs with those you had as you read the first pair. With your class, decide what words or groups of words in the second pair of paragraphs helped you most to feel just how sad and lonely the puppy was and then how excited he became later. You may want to make a list of them. Then decide what words or groups of words helped you most to imagine what you would have seen and heard if you had been there.

A Joke

Mother: Nancy, these cookies taste terrible!
Are you sure you followed the recipe?
Two cups of flour, a cup of sugar, a dash of salt —

Nancy: A dash of salt? Oh, dear! I thought it said a dish of salt!

WE MUST BE POLITE

(Lessons for children on how to behave under peculiar circumstances)

1

If we meet a gorilla
what shall we do?
Two things we may do
if we so wish to do.

Speak to the gorilla,
very, very respectfully,
"How do you do, sir?"

Or, speak to him with less
distinction of manner,
"Hey, why don't you go back
where you came from?"

2

If an elephant knocks on your door
and asks for something to eat,
there are two things to say:

Tell him there are nothing but cold
victuals in the house and he will do
better next door.

Or say: We have nothing but six bushels
of potatoes — will that be enough for
your breakfast, sir?

— CARL SANDBURG

DESERT TRADERS

by Iona Seibert Hiser

There are some interesting sights to see in the desert country of southwestern United States. In some places there are heaps of sticks, stones, and cactus that look as if someone had raked up a pile of junk and left it there. These piles are really homes, built by the white-throated wood rat, often called a pack rat or trade rat.

The pack rat is about six inches long, with a tail as long as it is. It has big eyes and large, rounded ears.

When a pack rat wants to build a nest, it finds a small hollow in the ground, often in a clump of cactus. It weaves together pieces of bark or grass to make a warm, thick-walled nest. The nest is lined with softer material to make a comfortable place for the babies.

Then the pack rat collects and piles on top of its nest any

kind of junk it can find. The junk may be pieces of old paper, sticks, stones, tin cans that some camper has thrown away, or—best of all—pieces of cactus.

Cactus is the pack rat's favorite material because the pieces are full of thorns. It would be a brave animal that tried to dig them away to get at the nest below. Yet somehow the little pack rat is able to carry and pile up the pieces of sharply spined cactus without hurting itself.

The little animals are called "pack rats" because they carry so many things in their mouths. In other words, they "pack" things around. They are called "trade rats" because they often swap whatever they are carrying for something else that attracts their attention. Perhaps one will drop a tin can in exchange for a bright silver spoon lying on a camper's table.

Pack rats can be a problem to campers because they carry off so many camp supplies. It is a good idea for campers in Arizona or New Mexico not to leave toothbrushes, soap, combs, and other small objects lying around where they can be carried away.

Pack rats try to carry away larger things, too. A camper in the mountains discovered one trying to make off with a man's shoe. Another one ate a neat half-circle out of a good felt hat! They've been known to take children's toys and store them in mounds over their nests. The nest mounds are often two or three feet high and five or six feet across.

The pack rats have good reasons for making their homes this way. They can make several tunnels through these mounds down to the real nest below. With so many openings to dart into from any direction, they have a better chance to escape whenever they are chased by an enemy.

The mounds also help the pack rats survive through the long, hot desert summer. During the hottest part of the day, they can keep cool by staying deep down inside the mounds.

Many animals have amazing ways of adjusting to the places where they live. The pack rat is a good example of such an animal.

AUTHOR

Mrs. Iona S. Hiser lives in Tucson, Arizona. When her two sons were very young, they used to take walks in the nearby desert. Often they would bring back such things as an orphaned baby squirrel, a little lizard, or a horned toad. Many of Mrs. Hiser's articles are about things her family found in the desert.

Her first book, *Desert Drama,* is about desert flowers and animals, and *From Scales to Fancy Feathers* is about birds. She has also written *The Coyote.* In all of her writings, Mrs. Hiser hopes to help her readers understand how important it is to protect wild animals.

What Is

Green is the grass
And the leaves of trees
Green is the smell
Of a country breeze.
Green is lettuce
And sometimes the sea.
When green is a feeling
You pronounce it N-V.
Green is a coolness
You get in the shade
Of the tall old woods
Where the moss is made.
Green is a flutter
That comes in Spring
When frost melts out
Of everything.
Green is a grasshopper
Green is jade
Green is hiding
In the shade —
Green is an olive
And a pickle.

Green?

The sound of green
Is a water-trickle
Green is the world
After the rain
Bathed and beautiful
Again.

April is green
Peppermint, too.
Every elf has
One green shoe.
Under a grape arbor
Air is green
With sprinkles of sunlight
In between.

Green is the meadow,
Green is the fuzz
That covers up
Where winter was.
Green is ivy and
Honeysuckle vine.
Green is yours
Green is mine. . . .

– MARY O'NEILL

Meg is a girl from Sweden, and this is one of her interesting adventures.

from Mischievous Meg

by Astrid Lindgren

Meg Experiments to See if She Is Clairvoyant

Meg had a friend named Albert Nilsson, and she couldn't think of a nicer place to visit than the Nilssons' kitchen. Albert often baked pretzels there for his family. He knew about so many things and told Meg wonderful stories while he went on with his baking. Meg would sit on the kitchen sofa, just listening. He had met only three robbers, but he had seen many ghosts. Meg had never seen a single one.

One day she asked him why this was. "It's because I'm clairvoyant," Albert replied. "You have to be. Otherwise you can't see ghosts."

Clairvoyant! That was a word Meg had never heard before, but Albert explained it to her. "If you're clairvoyant, it means that you have a special kind of eyes so that you can see ghosts when ordinary people can't."

"Perhaps I'm clairvoyant, too," Meg said eagerly. "Maybe I've just never been in a place where there are ghosts."

Albert burst out laughing. "You, clairvoyant! You're no more clairvoyant than a pig." Then he said, "But of course I could take you to the cemetery some dark night to test you."

Meg shuddered. "The cemetery — are there ghosts there?"

"You bet," said Albert. "I've seen ghosts in other places, too, but in the cemetery they are lined up in bands like tin soldiers. You can hardly move without bumping into one."

Meg would have liked very much to know whether she was clairvoyant, but she had no desire to go in the middle of the night to a cemetery swarming with ghosts. "Isn't there any place where there aren't quite so many of them?" she asked.

Albert's light blue eyes fixed her with a stare. "Are you a coward?"

Meg looked uncomfortable and didn't answer. It would be awful to have Albert think she was a coward, but worse still to go to the cemetery in the middle of the night.

Albert looked at her thoughtfully. "Of course I could meet you somewhere else," he said. "Our laundry, for example, is haunted."

"Is it?" Meg was amazed. She had been in the Nilssons' laundry many times, but she had never seen even the tiniest ghost. Could that mean that she really was no more clairvoyant than a pig?

"I don't think it's worth the trouble," Albert said, "but we could try just the same. Tonight, maybe?"

Meg squirmed uncomfortably. "Does it have to be at night?"

"Well, what do *you* think? Do you think the ghost helps Mother with the washing? No, midnight is the time he shows himself, not a minute before."

"Why does he hang around your laundry?" asked Meg.

Albert didn't answer for a while, and then he said, "Well, I may as well tell you the whole story. It's really a secret, and you have to promise not to say a word about it to a living soul."

Meg was so excited that she began to prickle with goose bumps.

Albert told her that the ghost was none other than his own grandfather's grandfather, who had lived a hundred years ago and was a very rich baron. Albert said he himself was practically a baron, though he kept it a secret. Meg gazed at him, her eyes big as saucers.

"Do you know why my grandfather's grandfather can't keep still like all the other old dead barons? Do you know why he has to roam around the laundry every night?"

Meg didn't know, but Albert could explain it. That rich old baron had buried a whole lot of money in his storeroom, which Mrs. Nilsson now used as a laundry.

"It was only for the fun of it," Albert said. "He had put so much money in the banks that there wasn't room for any more, and then he thought of the storeroom with the dirt floor. That's why his ghost is haunting this place."

Meg could hardly breathe. "Do you mean that the money is *here*?"

"Of course," said Albert.

Meg stared at him. "Why don't you dig it up?" she asked.

"Try to dig it up yourself and you'll see how easy it is. Do you know where to dig?"

No, of course Meg didn't know.

"Well, then," said Albert, as if that settled the matter.

Meg was looking at him as if she had never seen him before. There he stood, matter-of-factly making pretzels, although he was really a baron and had a grandfather's grandfather who was not only a baron, but also a ghost!

"What's his name, the ghost, your grandfather's grandfather, I mean?"

Albert stopped in the middle of twisting a pretzel. When he finally answered, it was as if he were reading out of a book: ". . . And his name was Baron Albert Nilsson . . . Crow."

"It's a good thing I'm not a snob," Albert went on. "The Right Honorable Baron Albert Nilsson Crow — that's what you should call me, actually. But it doesn't matter. You can keep on calling me Albert."

"Yes, because otherwise I couldn't talk to you," said Meg. "But I'll call you The Right Honorable Albert sometimes, if you like."

But Albert said he'd rather she didn't. All he wanted was to have Meg go with him to the laundry at midnight, because, if she should be clairvoyant, she could help to push Baron Crow into a corner. Then at last it might be possible to talk to him about the money. Albert had tried

several times, but his grandfather's grandfather had just disappeared through the wall with a faint, hollow sigh.

Meg was beginning to wonder whether it was really so important to be clairvoyant. She certainly would have liked to see a ghost, but not if she had to chase Albert's grandfather's grandfather around the Nilssons' laundry in the middle of the night.

"Mother would never allow me to go out in the middle of the night," she said.

"Silly, were you going to tell your mother?" Albert exclaimed. "Why, you'll never find out if you're clairvoyant. Believe me!"

Then Albert reminded her of all the times she had climbed out of her room by way of the porch roof. That had been during the day, of course, but what you could do in the daytime you could also do at night — if you weren't afraid to, that is.

"Well, are you coming or aren't you?" Albert asked severely. Meg didn't know what to say. "Maybe I wouldn't be able to stay awake until midnight," she said at last.

But Albert wasn't going to let her off so easily. He thought for a while and then said, "I think that I might be able to trick the old man into coming a little earlier, for once. Can you guess how?"

Meg couldn't. She wasn't as clever as Albert.

"I'll put my alarm clock in the laundry and set it ahead four hours. What do you think of that? Then the old man will think it's twelve o'clock when it's really only eight."

Meg laughed along with Albert, but she didn't sound very happy.

"Well, are you coming?" asked Albert more severely than before.

"Ye-e-es, I guess so," Meg said hesitantly.

"Fine," said Albert. "I can depend on you."

Will Baron Crow Appear?

If Albert could stand to see ghosts, so could Meg. At least, that's what she thought as long as she was lying in bed.

Meg had never gotten dressed in the dark before. She didn't dare turn on the light because her sister Betsy might wake up, or Mother might see the glimmer under the door. But Meg had put her clothes neatly on the chair next to her bed, so that she could get into them quickly.

Now she was ready for the worst part, and Meg clenched her teeth. She had to open the door and tiptoe across the hall to the little window that opened onto the porch roof, so quietly that Mother and Father wouldn't hear her.

She got to the window without any trouble and managed to open it, though there was a terrible squeak as she pushed it up. Meg crawled over the

porch roof, and she felt a pang of despair. She was leaving peace and warmth and safety behind, and ahead were only darkness and danger.

That dark, cold November night was gloomier than Meg could have believed possible. The wind that had sounded so gentle before now seemed to lash through the leafless trees, rattling the branches as if to frighten people.

Meg stood in the dark outside the Nilssons' kitchen window, looking in at Albert and his

mother and father. She would have loved to go inside where it was light and warm, but Albert had said that she was to stand by the window and make sounds like an owl. Meg did as she was told, and the sounds were so eerie that she even frightened herself. She saw Mrs. Nilsson jump with alarm. Albert too was startled. He got up from his chair, put his cap on, and went to the door.

He tiptoed over to where Meg was standing in the dark by the pear tree, and said in an excited whisper, "Now we'll see if we've managed to fool the old man into thinking it's twelve o'clock."

"Yes, w-we'll see," Meg said. "Did you put the alarm clock in the laundry?"

"Of course I did. I set it, too, so the old man won't oversleep. He isn't used to getting up at this hour."

A little worn path led to the laundry down by the river. Albert turned his flashlight on so Meg wouldn't stumble.

In the pitch blackness the laundry looked very much like a place ghosts would live in. When they reached the door, Albert turned the flashlight off.

"Tell me what you would like," he said. "I

thought you might like to see a ghost, but you don't have to if you don't want to."

Just then they heard the alarm clock go off in the laundry, as if it were trying to announce Meg's arrival and wake up all the ghosts. It was an awful sound.

"You can go home if you like," said Albert, "because it will take a while before Grandfather's Grandfather is fully awake."

Meg was trembling with fright, but how would she ever know whether she was clairvoyant if she didn't take this chance to find out?

"I *want* to see him," she mumbled, "but just for a second."

"Well, then," said Albert, "don't blame me if you get so scared you pass out."

He turned the key, and the door slowly opened with a horrible creak that would certainly have wakened Baron Crow if by any chance he hadn't heard the alarm clock.

Meg stared into the blackness and grabbed hold of Albert's sweater. Without him she would be lost, and she knew it. "Turn on the flashlight so we can see," she pleaded.

But Albert didn't turn on the flashlight. "You're not very used to seeing ghosts, that's sure. Nothing makes them madder than having a flashlight pointed at them. It makes them growl. Have you ever heard a ghost growl?"

Fortunately, Meg never had.

"You're lucky," said Albert. "I know someone who did, and he's still shaking."

Meg decided that Albert knew best, and she followed him into the pitch darkness. Albert closed the door behind him, and they couldn't see a thing. Baron Crow was probably standing in the midst of the blackness, waiting for them. He'd be terrifying enough even if he wasn't growling. They stood motionless just inside the door, waiting.

Then Meg heard Albert catch his breath.

"There he comes, there, over by the wall!"

Meg screamed and closed her eyes.

"Do you see him?" Albert whispered.

Meg opened her eyes reluctantly and looked in the direction of the wall. She couldn't see a thing, only blackness. Albert was probably right. She wasn't any more clairvoyant than a pig, and at that moment she was thankful for it.

"Don't you really see him?" whispered Albert. "Don't you see a white, nasty-looking thing with a sort of halo around it?"

"No," said Meg truthfully.

"That's strange," said Albert. There was no doubt that Albert could see him clearly, and talk to him, too.

"Right Honorable Baron, where have you hidden the money? Answer me! That is, if you want to."

But there was no sound. The Baron didn't seem to want to answer.

"He's stubborn, as usual," Albert whispered to Meg. He added in a loud voice, "I'm a baron myself and could use the money. Please, Grandfather's Grandfather, we're relatives, after all!"

Then he whispered to Meg again, "Can't you really see him? He looks just awful."

"No," Meg insisted. "I guess I'm not clairvoyant."

"Don't be so sure," said Albert. "Sometimes it can take quite a while before you get started. And then, one, two, three, you see ghosts all over the place."

But Meg was quite sure that she wasn't clairvoyant, and the only thing she wanted was to get out of the laundry. Albert whispered, "Look, he's motioning to me. He wants me to come. Yes, Grandfather's Grandfather, I'm coming."

But Meg clung to Albert's sweater. "Please don't leave me," she whispered, terrified.

"I have to," whispered Albert. "He wants to show me where the money is. Stay here. Don't move."

Suddenly Meg was alone in the dark. She heard Albert tiptoe across the floor and didn't know what to do. She didn't dare try to follow him, and she didn't dare to stay where she was.

"Albert," she called. "Albert!"

But Albert didn't answer. He had disappeared into the darkness.

"Albert," she wailed. "Albert, I want to go home!"

Then she saw something. Oh, horror, she *was* clairvoyant after all! She saw a white, terrible thing with a sort of halo around it. Baron Crow was standing over by the wall, as sure as anything.

Then Meg screamed as she had never screamed in her life. She screamed and screamed and groped for the door, trying to get out. The light around Baron Crow went out, and she couldn't see him any more. Still she went on screaming. Albert's voice came out of the darkness.

"Quiet, Meg, don't scream like that! You're frightening Baron Crow."

But Meg didn't hear a word. She was frantic, and all she wanted was to get out — OUT!

Albert and the "Ghost Money"

Alva, the woman who worked for Meg's family, had come back from town, where she had spent the evening. She was just about to put the key in the kitchen door when Meg came racing across the lawn. Without a word, Meg threw her arms around Alva so violently that Alva was almost knocked over.

"What on earth are you doing out at this time of night?" Alva asked.

Meg only moaned, and Alva could feel her whole body trembling. Alva didn't ask any more questions but quickly led Meg into the kitchen and turned on the light.

"What on earth has happened?" Alva asked. She took Meg in her arms and sat down on the kitchen sofa, rocking her gently.

"Alva, I've seen a ghost," Meg whispered. "Oh, Alva, I'm *clairvoyant*!"

It was some time before Alva could get anything more out of her. She was in such a state that she could hardly talk. Besides, Albert had said she mustn't tell a living soul. But she had to tell *someone*. Finally Alva heard the whole story about Baron Crow in the Nilssons' laundry. She flew into a rage.

"That Albert! He's going to catch it! Him and his ghosts!" Alva stormed.

But Meg defended him. "He can't help being clairvoyant."

"Oh, can't he!" said Alva furiously. "Just wait till I've finished with him! Then he won't be clairvoyant any longer, I promise you. The Right Honorable Albert, indeed!"

Fortunately Mother and Father were already asleep, and Alva promised to tell them nothing. "If your mother hears about this, you've been to the Nilssons' for the last time. Besides, I think you've had punishment enough. But I'm going to give Albert a talking-to that he won't forget."

The next day, when Meg came home from school, Albert was leaning on the fence as if he were waiting for someone. Alva must have given him a piece of her mind, because he looked very shamefaced.

He whistled, and Meg went over to him. "I had no idea that you were *that* clairvoyant," he said, "or I never would have taken you along to the laundry."

Meg shuddered at the mention of the laundry. "I'm never going there again."

"Why not?" Albert asked her. "You don't have to be afraid of Grandfather's Grandfather. He won't come any more."

"How do you know?" asked Meg.

"Because he is through with being a ghost. I've dug up the money."

"You have?" said Meg.

"Yes, but it's a secret, so don't go and tell Alva."

Feeling ashamed, Meg promised not to tell.

She looked curiously at Albert. "Are you rich now?"

Albert looked thoughtfully at the ground. "Well, I think that Grandfather's Grandfather has made an awful lot of fuss for only two-fifty." He put his hand in his pocket and pulled out the money.

"Was that all?" asked Meg.

"Yes, that was all. But remember that Grandfather's Grandfather lived more than a hundred years ago. At that time two-fifty was not to be sneezed at, so no wonder he's been hanging around." Albert put a fifty-cent piece in Meg's hand. "Here, this is for your mental anguish, or whatever it's called."

Meg beamed. Albert *was* nice, after all. "Thank you, Albert. You're awfully kind."

"You're welcome. It's ghost money, but it's just as good as ordinary money."

Then the Right Honorable Albert disappeared into his kitchen. Meg was left standing there, very much pleased with her ghost money.

"Just think — it's been buried in Nilssons' laundry over a hundred years, but still it's shiny and looks real!" she thought.

AUTHOR

The story you have just read is a chapter from *Mischievous Meg,* by Astrid Lindgren.

Mrs. Lindgren is from Sweden. When her two children were very young, they were always begging her to tell them stories. One time her daughter was recovering from pneumonia. She asked her mother to tell her "a story about Pippi Longstocking." Mrs. Lindgren made up a story to tell her, but she had never thought of writing down any of the stories she told her children.

Then one snowy day, Mrs. Lindgren was taking a walk. She fell and broke her ankle, and she had to stay in bed for a week. Since she had nothing else to do, she began to write down the stories she had told her daughter. This later became a very successful book, *Pippi Longstocking.*

Since then, Mrs. Lindgren has written many books in the Swedish language. Most have been translated into other languages so that they can be enjoyed by children throughout the world. Besides *Pippi Longstocking* and *Mischievous Meg,* you might also enjoy reading *Children on Troublemaker Street, Rasmus and the Vagabond,* and *Tomten.*

Astrid Lindgren has won many honors for her writing. She was the first children's author ever to receive the Swedish State Award, in 1956. In 1958 she won the Hans Christian Andersen Medal for her outstanding writing.

MORE BOOKS TO ENJOY

THE ALLIGATOR CASE, *by William Pène du Bois.*
A boy detective uses a "trap-trap" to catch three criminals in this very funny story.

THE BAD CHILD'S BOOK OF BEASTS, *by Hilaire Belloc.*
You'll have fun with these nonsense poems about animals.

DESERT PEOPLE, *by Ann Nolan Clark.*
This interesting book tells about the Indians who live in the southwestern part of the United States.

THE MELLOPS GO DIVING FOR TREASURE, *by Tomi Ungerer.*
A family of French pigs sails the seas in search of a buried treasure.

THE MOUSE AND THE MOTORCYCLE, *by Beverly Cleary.*
A mouse causes a real uproar (and has a wonderful time!) when he learns to ride a toy motorcycle.

TALES FROM MOOMINVALLEY, *by Tove Jansson.*
This is one book in a Swedish series about a family of little creatures called Moomins.

THE TROUBLE WITH JENNY'S EAR, *by Oliver Butterworth.*
A clairvoyant girl amazes everyone when she appears on a TV quiz show.

GLOSSARY

This glossary can help you find out meanings and pronunciations of words in this book that you may not know. The meanings of the words as they are used in this book are always given. Often you will also find other common meanings listed.

You can find out the correct pronunciation of any glossary word by using the special spelling after the word and the pronunciation key. The *Full Pronunciation Key* below shows how to pronounce each consonant and vowel in a special spelling. There is also a short form of this full key at the bottom of every left-hand page in the glossary.

Full Pronunciation Key

Consonant Sounds

/b/	**b**i**b**	/k/	**k**ic**k**	/sh/	**sh**ip, di**sh**
/ch/	**ch**ur**ch**	/l/	**l**id, need**le**	/t/	**t**igh**t**
/d/	**d**i**d**	/m/	**m**an, a**m**	/th/	**th**in, pa**th**
/f/	**f**ast, o**ff**	/n/	**n**o, sudd**en**	/*th*/	**th**is, ba**the**
/g/	**g**a**g**	/ng/	thi**ng**	/v/	**v**ine, ca**ve**
/h/	**h**at	/p/	**p**o**p**	/w/	**w**ith
/hw/	**wh**ich	/r/	**r**oa**r**	/y/	**y**es
/j/	**j**u**dge**	/s/	**s**ee, mi**ss**	/z/	**z**ebra, si**ze**
		/zh/	plea**s**ure		

Vowel Sounds

/ă/	p**a**t	/ĭ/	p**i**t	/oi/	n**oi**se
/ā/	p**ay**	/ī/	p**ie**	/ou/	**ou**t
/âr/	c**are**	/îr/	f**ier**ce	/o͝o/	t**oo**k
/ä/	f**a**ther	/ŏ/	p**o**t	/o͞o/	b**oo**t
/ĕ/	p**e**t	/ō/	t**oe**	/ŭ/	c**u**t
/ē/	b**e**	/ô/	p**aw**, f**o**r	/ûr/	t**ur**n
		/yo͞o/	**u**se		

/ə/ **a**bout, sil**e**nt, penc**i**l, lem**o**n, circ**u**s

This pronunciation key is adapted from *The American Heritage Dictionary of the English Language*, published by American Heritage Publishing Co., Inc., and Houghton Mifflin Company.

A

ad•just (ə-jŭst′) 1. Change so as to be correct or workable. 2. Become suited and used to where one lives.

ad•mi•ral (ăd′mər-əl) High officer in the Navy.

ad•ven•ture (ăd-vĕn′chər) 1. Unusual happening. 2. Exciting, perhaps dangerous, deed.

air•shaft (âr′shăft) Walled-in open space down through the middle of a building to let in air.

a•muse (ə-myo͞oz′) 1. Keep someone from getting bored or restless. 2. Cause to laugh or smile.

an•guish (ăng′gwĭsh) Grief; torment; great pain.

an•noy (ə-noi′) Bother; disturb; vex.

ap•plause (ə-plôz′) Clapping of hands to show enjoyment.

ap•point•ment (ə-point′mənt) 1. Arrangement to meet at a certain time and place. 2. Naming of someone to fill a certain office or position: *He received an appointment from the President.*

ap•prove (ə-pro͞ov′) 1. Agree to. 2. Think well of.

aq•ua•naut (ăk′wə-nôt) Person trained to explore underwater for scientific purposes.

arch (ärch) 1. Part of a bridge or building that is curved at the top. 2. Bend into a curve.

as•sis•tant (ə-sĭs′tənt) Helper.

at•tract (ə-trăkt′) 1. Cause to come or look toward oneself. 2. Be pleasing to.

a•ware (ə-wâr′) Knowing about: *He's aware of his mistake.*

awk•ward (ôk′wərd) 1. Clumsy; not graceful in movement. 2. Uneasy: *an awkward feeling around strangers.*

B

bab•ble (băb′əl) 1. Continuing speechlike sounds that the hearer cannot understand. 2. Make such sounds.

ă pat / ā pay / âr care / ä father / ĕ pet / ē be / ĭ pit / ī pie / îr fierce / ŏ pot / ō toe / ô paw, for / oi noise / ou out / o͝o took / o͞o boot / th thin / *th* this / ŭ cut / ûr turn / yo͞o use / ə about / zh pleasure

bar•on (băr′ən) Title given to a man whose lands were given his family by the king.

beech (bēch) Kind of nut tree.

beg•gar (bĕg′ər) Person who asks others for cash or food.

bel•low (bĕl′ō) 1. Cry out or shout in a deep voice. 2. Loud cry.

bleach•ers (blē′chərz) Uncovered bench seats for people watching outdoor sports.

blend (blĕnd) 1. Mix together. 2. Seem to be the same color: *A chameleon blends with the leaf it is sitting on.*

bliz•zard (blĭz′ərd) Heavy snowstorm with very strong winds.

brisk (brĭsk) Lively; quick.

but•ter•fly valve (bŭt′ər-flī vălv) Part of a car's engine that controls the flow of air between the air filter and the carburetor. It is so called because it looks somewhat like a butterfly's wings when in motion.

C

cap•sule (kăp′səl) Airtight object used to transport aquanauts or astronauts in certain explorations.

car•a•van (kăr′ə-văn) Group of people traveling together, often across a desert.

car•bu•re•tor (kär′bə-rā-tər) Part of the car where gasoline and air are mixed.

cer•e•mo•ny (sĕr′ə-mō-nē) Act performed because of custom or politeness.

chore (chôr) Small job, especially around a house or farm.

chow•der (chou′dər) Thick soup, often made of fish, clams, vegetables, and milk.

clair•voy•ant (klâr-voi′ənt) Having the power to see or hear things that others cannot.

clench (klĕnch) Close tightly together.

com•pli•ment (kŏm′plə-mənt) 1. Say something nice about someone. 2. Statement praising someone.

com•pos•er (kəm-pō′zər) Person who writes music.

con•di•tion (kən-dĭsh′ən) 1. State of health or well-being of a person or thing: *That bike is in poor condition.* 2. Something that must happen in order for something else to take place.

con•stit•u•ent (kən-stĭch′o͞o-ənt) Person represented by an elected leader: *A state's governor has to think of all his constituents.*

con•vince (kən-vĭns′) Persuade; make a person believe something.

coun•cil (koun′səl) Group of people called together to give advice and help solve problems.

cup•board (kŭb′ərd) Small closet with shelves for dishes and food.

D

dame (dām) *Slang.* Woman; girl.

dan•gle (dăng′gəl) Hang or swing loosely.

de•cent (dē′sənt) Proper; suitable to one's needs: *a decent meal.*

de•coy (dē′koi) 1. Something used to trick a person or animal: *A wooden duck placed on a lake to attract live ducks is a decoy.* 2. Lead into danger by means of a trick.

de•lude (dĭ-lo͞od′) Mislead; trick.

de•sign (dĭ-zīn′) 1. Invent; make a plan for. 2. Drawing. 3. Pattern of lines or colors. 4. Plan. 5. Purpose.

de•spair (dĭ-spâr′) 1. Loss of all hope. 2. Give up; lose hope completely.

de•ter•mined (dĭ-tûr′mĭnd) Having one's mind firmly made up.

dis•tinct (dĭs-tingkt′) 1. Different from others; unlike. 2. Clear; easily seen or heard.

dose (dōs) Certain amount of medicine to be taken at one time.

dune (do͞on) Hill of sand made by the wind.

E

ee•rie (îr′ē) Mysterious; strange; frightening.

el•e•vat•ed (ĕl′ə-vā-tĭd) 1. Lifted up. 2. Train that runs on tracks built over a street.

---

en•vy (ĕn′vē) 1. Feeling of unhappiness because of someone else's good fortune: *"Being green with envy" is a common saying.* 2. Person or object that brings on such a feeling: *Her good looks were the envy of all her friends.* 3. Wish for what is someone else's: *We all envy Joe's success.*

ex•haust (ĕg-zôst′) 1. Completely tire or wear out. 2. Empty out. 3. Use up.

ex•press (ĕk-sprĕs′) 1. Fast train that does not make stops at every station on its way. 2. Tell; make known. 3. Sent by fast and direct means. 4. Plainly stated: *an express wish.*

F

fee (fē) Payment for a service or for a job done.

fil•ter (fĭl′tər) Substance or object through which liquid or air can pass to become cleaned. 2. Pass something through such a substance.

flab•ber•gast (flăb′ər-găst) Thoroughly amaze by doing or saying something completely unexpected.

flat•ter (flăt′ər) More flat.

flat•ter (flăt′ər) Say pleasing things to someone in order to get something.

flight (flīt) 1. Act of flying. 2. Group of birds traveling together through the air. 3. Airline trip. 4. Stairs leading from one floor to another.

flight (flīt) Escape: *He explained his sudden flight from the woods by claiming he saw a bear.*

flinch (flĭnch) 1. Draw back in fear or pain. 2. Make a sudden, surprised movement.

flung (flŭng) 1. Suddenly and forcefully thrown. 2. Threw with force.

for•tu•nate (fôr′chə-nĭt) Lucky.

frost•bit•ten (frôst′bĭt-n) Partly frozen and numb.

G

gash (găsh) 1. Make a long, deep cut. 2. Wound made by a deep cut.

gear (gîr) 1. Clothing or tools needed for a certain purpose. 2. Part of a car which enables the driver to control speed or direction.

glare (glâr) 1. Shine very brightly. 2. Angry, fixed stare. 3. Look angrily. 4. Very bright or blinding light.

glim•mer (glĭm′ər) 1. Faint, dim light. 2. Give off a soft light.

gram (grăm) Unit of measure of weight often used by scientists: *There are about 28 grams in one ounce.*

grope (grōp) Feel one's way in the dark.

guest (gĕst) 1. One who is visiting another. 2. Performer making a special appearance on a show.

gull (gŭl) Kind of water bird.

gust (gŭst) Sudden rush of wind.

H

ha•lo (hā′lō) Ring of light.

haul (hôl) 1. Pull or drag with force. 2. Carry from one place to another. **—haul alongside.** Come on over.

hoarse (hôrs) Husky; rough-sounding.

hor•ri•fy (hôr′ə-fī) Frighten or shock terribly.

hos•tile (hŏs′təl) 1. Unfriendly. 2. Having to do with an enemy.

hov•er (hŭv′ər) 1. Stay in one place in the air by beating the wings. 2. Stay close by.

hud•dle (hŭd′əl) 1. Crowd closely together. 2. Closely crowded group. 3. Short gathering together of football players to plan the next play.

hum•ble (hŭm′bəl) 1. Aware of one's own faults. 2. Not proud. 3. Not of a wealthy class. 4. Respectful; timid. 5. Make someone feel ashamed.

hunch (hŭnch) 1. Strong, but unexplainable, feeling: *I had a hunch something was going to happen.* 2. Bend or draw up into a rounded hump.

I

im•press (ĭm-prĕs′) Cause someone to admire or think well of oneself or one's ideas.

ă pat / ā pay / âr care / ä father / ĕ pet / ē be / ĭ pit / ī pie / îr fierce / ŏ pot / ō toe / ô paw, for / oi noise / ou out / o͝o took / o͞o boot / th thin / *th* this / ŭ cut / ûr turn / yo͞o use / ə about / zh pleasure

in•stance (ĭn′stəns) 1. Case: *In this instance I think it was wise to call off the game.* 2. Example. 3. Request: *She set the table at the instance of her mother.* **—for instance.** For example.

in•stru•ment (ĭn′strə-mənt) 1. Object that can be played to make music. 2. Tool, such as one used by a doctor or dentist.

in•tent (ĭn-tĕnt′) 1. Aim; purpose. 2. Having one's mind closely fixed on something: *He's intent on his work.*

in•ter•rupt (ĭn-tə-rŭpt′) 1. Break in and start to speak while someone else is still talking. 2. Make something stop for a while: *The rain interrupted our game for an hour.*

in•vis•i•ble (ĭn-vĭz′ə-bəl) Impossible to be seen.

in•volve (ĭn-vŏlv′) 1. Bring one into: *Don't involve me in the argument.* 2. Have as a necessary part: *Being a good ball player involves a lot of practice.*

J

jag•ged (jăg′ĭd) Having a very rough, sharp-pointed surface or edge.

joint (joint) 1. Place where two parts of a machine or body are joined. 2. Large piece of meat used for roasting. 3. Used or done by two or more: *a joint undertaking.*

K

keen (kēn) 1. Sharp; with a fine cutting edge. 2. Bright; smart. 3. Eager; enthusiastic: *a keen desire to go.* 4. *Slang.* Fine; good-looking.

knap•sack (năp′săk) Bag for storing things that is carried by a traveler.

knight (nīt) In olden times, a man who served a king and performed brave deeds: *A knight often wore a suit of armor for protection.*

L

lame (lām) 1. Unable to walk well because of a hurt leg. 2. Weak; poor: *a lame excuse.*

larch (lärch) Tree of the pine family.

lash (lăsh) 1. Blow strongly against. 2. Eyelash. 3. Strike with a whip. 4. Beat harshly; scold severely.

live•stock (līv′stŏk) Farm animals.

lo•cate (lō′kāt) 1. Find where something is. 2. Settle in a certain place.

M

med•i•cate (mĕd′ə-kāt) Treat with medicine.

midst (mĭdst) Middle part. **—in the midst of.** Surrounded by.

mis•chie•vous (mĭs′chə-vəs) Playful; teasing, often to the point of being troublesome.

mi•ser (mī′zər) Person who loves money and is not generous about spending it.

mo•tion (mō′shən) 1. Movement. 2. Make a signal, often with a hand. 3. In club meetings, a suggestion that has to be voted on.

mud•dle (mŭd′l) 1. Confuse. 2. Mix up; make a mess. 3. Act in a stupid way.

N

ne•on (nē′ŏn) Colorless gas found in tiny amounts in the air. When charged with electricity, it gives off a colored glow. Therefore it is often encased in clear glass tubes and used for signs.

net (nĕt) 1. Fish trap made of loosely woven string. 2. Any loosely woven cloth. 3. Catch in a net.

net (nĕt) 1. Bring in a gain of: *We'll need to net at least three runs in the next two innings.* 2. Left after necessary subtractions: *After we paid our expenses, we had a net profit of $400.*

nu•mis•mat•ics (nōō-mĭz-măt′ĭks) Study and collecting of coins.

P

pang (păng) Sudden, sharp feeling of fear, sadness, or pain.

ă pat / ā pay / âr care / ä father / ĕ pet / ē be / ĭ pit / ī pie / îr fierce / ŏ pot / ō toe / ô paw, for / oi noise / ou out / ŏŏ took / ōō boot / th thin / *th* this / ŭ cut / ûr turn / yōō use / ə about / zh pleasure

peas•ant (pĕz′ənt) One of a class of people who are farm workers or own small farms.

pen•i•cil•lin (pĕn-ə-sĭl′ĭn) Kind of medicine used to treat many types of illness.

perch (pûrch) 1. Bar, branch, or pole where birds rest. 2. Sit or put in a high place. 3. Any high seat.

perch (pûrch) Small, fresh-water fish.

per•suade (pər-swād′) Win over to one's way of thinking by reasoning or argument.

pe•ti•tion (pə-tĭsh′ən) 1. Written paper asking for something. 2. Ask for something in writing.

plot (plŏt) 1. Small piece of ground. 2. Secret plan. 3. Outline of happenings in a book, play, or story. 4. Make secret plans. 5. Plan for a story.

plunge (plŭnj) 1. Move quickly forward or downward; thrust. 2. Dive.

pneu•mo•nia (nōō-mōn′yə) Serious lung disease.

pounce (pouns) 1. Leap down upon. 2. Jump suddenly and grab.

prac•ti•cal•ly (prăk′tĭk-lē) 1. In a sensible way. 2. Through real experience. 3. *All right in everyday talk.* Almost.

pro•ceed (prō-sēd′) 1. Go onward. 2. Begin and carry out: *Let's proceed with the plan.*

prod (prŏd) 1. Poke with something pointed. 2. Urge to go forward. 3. Something used to poke with.

pro•fes•sor (prə-fĕs′ər) Teacher in a college.

R

ra•di•a•tor (rā′dē-ā-tər) 1. Something used to heat a room or building, often a set of pipes through which hot water or steam can move. 2. Part of a car that holds water to keep the engine from overheating.

razz (răz) *Slang.* Tease; make fun of.

reck•on (rĕk′ən) 1. Count; figure: *Don't forget to reckon on the cost of the wood.* 2. *All right in everyday talk.* Think; suppose.

re•luc•tant (rĭ-lŭk′tənt) Unwilling; hesitant.

rep•re•sent (rĕp-rĭ-zĕnt′) 1. Act for; stand for: *The President represents the people of the United States.* 2. Play the part of.

re•quest (rĭ-kwĕst′) 1. Ask for politely. 2. Something asked for. 3. Act of asking for something.

re•spect (rĭ-spĕkt′) 1. Look up to; think highly of. 2. Admiration; politeness. 3. Obey. 4. Way: *In that respect, I must admit that he is better for the job than I am.*

rhythm (rĭ*th*′əm) 1. Regular repeating of a beat, as in music. 2. Rise and fall of sounds, as in poetry when read aloud.

roost (ro͞ost) 1. Perch for a bird. 2. Rest or sleep on something like a perch.

rus•tle (rŭs′əl) 1. Soft, quick, whispering sound. 2. Make a soft whispering sound.

rus•tle (rŭs′əl) Steal cattle.

S

sep•a•rate (sĕp′ə-rāt) Take or pull apart; keep apart.

sep•a•rate (sĕp′ər-ĭt) Single; not together; by itself.

shan't (shănt) Shall not.

shin (shĭn) Front part of the leg between the knee and the ankle.

shove (shŭv) 1. Thrust; push with sudden force. 2. Rough, sudden push.

sig•na•ture (sĭg′nə-cho͝or) Name of someone as written by that person.

sire (sīr) 1. Father. 2. When capitalized, a title of respect given a king.

slang (slăng) Name given to certain word usage that is not really correct in formal writing, but is commonly used and is all right in everyday talk.

slit (slĭt) 1. Make a narrow cut as with a knife. 2. Long, narrow cut or tear.

ă pat / ā pay / âr care / ä father / ĕ pet / ē be / ĭ pit / ī pie / îr fierce / ŏ pot / ō toe / ô paw, for / oi noise / ou out / o͝o took / o͞o boot / th thin / *th* this / ŭ cut / ûr turn / yo͞o use / ə about / zh pleasure

slosh (slŏsh) 1. Make a splashing sound. 2. Sound of liquid splashing.

snarl (snärl) 1. Growl while showing the teeth. 2. Speak in an angry, growling tone.

snarl (snärl) Tangle.

snob (snŏb) Person who feels superior to many others.

so•lu•tion (sə-lo͞o′shən) 1. Liquid mixture. 2. Answer to a problem or mystery.

soothe (so͞o*th*) Make comfortable or calm.

sow (sō) Scatter seed for planting.

sow (sou) Female pig.

spe•cial•ize (spĕsh′ə-līz) Work on one certain part of a job, hobby, or field of study: *He's going to specialize on stamps of the African countries.*

spin•ney (spĭn′ē) Thicket of small bushes or trees.

spy (spī) 1. Person who secretly watches others. 2. Catch sight of.

squar•ish (skwâr′ĭsh) Shaped somewhat like a square.

squire (skwīr) 1. Country gentleman, usually a wealthy landowner. 2. In olden times, a young man who was a knight's assistant.

stag•ger (stăg′ər) 1. Move or walk in an unsteady way. 2. Unsteady way of walking. 3. Strike with surprise: *The news staggered him.*

stride (strīd) 1. Way of walking or running with long steps. 2. Walk or run with long steps. 3. Single long step.

stu•pen•dous (sto͞o-pĕn′dəs) 1. Wonderful. 2. Amazingly large.

sub•way (sŭb′wā) Underground railroad found in some large cities.

sul•fa•di•a•zine (sŭl-fə-dī′ə-zēn) Kind of medicine used to treat pneumonia and other illnesses.

su•pe•ri•or (sə-pîr′ē-ər) 1. Proud of being above others in some way. 2. Higher; better. 3. Excellent; of great value.

surf (sûrf) Waves of the sea as they break on the shore.

sur•face (sûr′fəs) Outside or top part of anything: *The surface of a body of water is where the water meets the air.*

sur•vive (sər-vīv′) 1. Stay alive. 2. Live longer than.

swab (swŏb) 1. Mop for cleaning floors. 2. Clean with a mop. 3. *Slang.* Sailor.

swag•ger (swăg′ər) Walk or talk in a show-off manner.

T

tac•tics (tăk′tĭks) 1. Clever way of getting what one wants. 2. Plan of action.

task (tăsk) Job; piece of work.

tem•per•a•men•tal (tĕm-prə-mĕnt′l) Easily angered or excited.

ten•ant (tĕn′ənt) Person who pays rent to live in a house, farm or apartment owned by another.

thatch (thăch) 1. Roof made of straw or leaves. 2. Straw or leaves used to make a roof. 3. Make a roof of straw or leaves.

thresh (thrĕsh) Separate grain or seeds from straw by beating.

ti•rade (tī′rād) Long, angry, scolding speech.

to•ken (tō′kən) 1. Piece of metal used in place of money on buses, subway trains, and the like. 2. Sign: *The gift was a token of his friendship.*

tor•rent (tôr′ənt) Forceful, rushing stream.

tramp (trămp) 1. Walk heavily. 2. Person who moves around aimlessly from place to place. 3. Sound of heavy footsteps.

tres•pass (trĕs′păs) Go onto someone else's property or anywhere one shouldn't be.

tribe (trīb) Group of people who live together and share the same leader and way of life.

trough (trôf) Long, narrow, open box used to hold food or water for animals.

turn•stile (tûrn′stīl) Post set in an entrance with arms coming out from the middle. To get through the entrance, a person drops a coin or token into a slot, and the arms turn to let the person go through.

ă pat / ā pay / âr care / ä father / ĕ pet / ē be / ĭ pit / ī pie / îr fierce / ŏ pot / ō toe / ô paw, for / oi noise / ou out / o͝o took / o͞o boot / th thin / *th* this / ŭ cut / ûr turn / yo͞o use / ə about / zh pleasure

U

un•a•ware (ŭn-ə-wâr′) Not knowing or realizing.

un•con•vinced (ŭn-kən-vĭnst′) Unbelieving.

un•for•tu•nate (ŭn-for′chə-nĭt) Unlucky.

V

valve (vălv) Movable part that controls the flow of a gas or liquid in a machine. See also **butterfly valve.**

vast (văst) Huge; of great size.

vi•o•lent (vī′ə-lənt) Caused by unusually severe force that is often unexpected.

vot•er (vōt′ər) One who helps to elect a leader or to decide what should be done in a matter that concerns everyone.

W

wail (wāl) 1. Cry long and loudly. 2. Long, loud crying.

woe•be•gone (wō′bĭ-gôn) Sad-looking.

wound (wo͞ond) 1. Hurt place on the skin caused by a cut, stab, or shot. 2. Hurt by breaking the skin. 3. Hurt by saying something unkind.

wound (wound) Wrapped; twisted; tangled.

wreck•age (rĕk′ĭj) Disorder caused by things having been broken and destroyed.

Y

youth (yo͞oth) 1. Early time of life; younger days. 2. Young person, especially a young man. 3. Young people.

Artist Credits

WILLI BAUM *(Cover, title page, and magazine covers, pages 7, 109, 237)*

Illustrations: CAROL ANTHONY *(page 185)*; WILLI BAUM *(pages 240–262)*; FRANK BOZZO *(pages 224–225)*; MARC BROWN *(page 111)*; KEVIN CALLAHAN *(pages 66–80)*; KINUKO CRAFT *(pages 140–157)*; HERBERT DANSKA *(pages 186–197)*; LORRAINE FOX *(pages 9–26)*; JOHN FREAS *(pages 60, 282–283)*; MARYLIN HAFNER *(pages 28–39)*; JOHN HAM *(pages 61–65, 90–94, 167–171, 216–222, 263, 277–280, 309–313)*; DAVE JONAS *(pages 42–59)*; HILARY KNIGHT *(pages 296–308)*; GORDON KIBBEE *(page 239)*; DORA LEDER *(pages 264, 322–345)*; ELAINE LIVERMORE *(page 95)*; KENNETH LONGTEMPS *(pages 265–276)*; JULES MAIDOFF *(pages 96–107)*; IKKI MATSUMOTO *(pages 40–41)*; DAVID MCPHAIL *(pages 81, 174–184, 314–315)*; BILL MORRISON *(pages 284–294)*; DEL NICHOLS *(pages 112–136)*; ALFRED OLSCHEWSKI *(page 295)*; PETER PARNALL *(pages 316–319)*; KAREN PELLATON *(page 173)*; JERRY PINKNEY *(pages 206–215)*; MARTY RICHARDSON *(page 281)*; DR. SEUSS *(pages 200–205)*; ERNEST H. SHEPARD *(pages 226–235)*; CECILE WEBSTER *(pages 320–321)*; JOYCE WINKLE *(layout for pages 160–166)*.

Photographs: AMERICAN NUMISMATIC SOCIETY *(pages 84, 86, 87)*; ERIK ANDERSON *(page 223)*; BUREAU OF THE MINT TREASURY DEPARTMENT *(page 87)*; THE CHASE MANHATTAN BANK MUSEUM OF MONEYS OF THE WORLD, NEW YORK *(page 83)*; CULVER PICTURES, INC. *(pages 160, 162–165, 166)*; ARTHUR FURST *(page 198)*; GENERAL ELECTRIC COMPANY'S RE-ENTRY AND ENVIRONMENTAL SYSTEMS DIVISION, OCEANS SYSTEMS PROGRAMS *(pages 138–139)*; GEORGE MARTIN (DPI) *(page 161)*; NATIONAL BANK OF DETROIT *(pages 86, 88)*; SMITHSONIAN INSTITUTION *(page 85)*; ROBERT SWEDROE *(pages 27, 172)*; UNITED FRUIT COMPANY *(page 171)*; WESTERN WAYS FEATURES *(pages 158–159)*; WHITMAN HOBBY DEPARTMENT, WESTERN PUBLISHING COMPANY, INC. *(pages 82, 85, 86, 88)*; WIDE WORLD *(page 166)*.

NORMAN ROCKWELL *(painting)* COURTESY OF NATIONAL BASEBALL HALL OF FAME AND MUSEUM, INC. *(page 137)*.

FGHIJKLM-KR-7987654321